FOR THE LOVE OF ROBIN
(and all disabled people including
their unsung heroes, the carers)

FOR THE LOVE OF ROBIN

Dorothea Wood-Z'Berg

Book Guild Publishing
Sussex, England

First published in Great Britain in 2006 by
The Book Guild Ltd
Pavilion View
19 New Road
Brighton, East Sussex
BN1 1UF

Typesetting in Times by
Keyboard Services, Luton, Bedfordshire

Printed in Great Britain by
Antony Rowe Ltd, Chippenham, Wiltshire

A catalogue record for this book is available from
The British Library

ISBN 978 1 84624 067 6

In every carer's heart pulsates a piece of Mother Teresa;
In a disabled person's heart, the hopes of a mountain-climbing Hillary.

Contents

ix

Foreword

There are millions of disabled people in this world and millions of loving carers behind them. Some disabled people have found a loving relationship; some have got married and even been able to raise a family. Not all are so lucky. When in an institution or care home, they can only watch the normal expected life pass by. To be loved and share life with someone you love, to go out whenever you want to do your own shopping, go to a play or other amusement, to own a house or take part in bringing up a child, is way out of reach. The carers who care for these people are unsung heroes; they share their charges' emotional feelings and bear with them in their frustrations. They support where often the family has abandoned them.

This book is written as a tribute to all loving carers and disabled people who have the courage to live life as best as they can.

I have mentioned as many disabling conditions that I have come in contact with myself as a nurse, and in my personal life with relations, friends and neighbours. A list of helpful associations and charities for most of the disabling conditions mentioned, with their phone numbers, some of which are free, emails and web sites, is at the back of the book.

Thankful Acknowledgements

(And kind contributions by)

Chambers Dictionary (1999 Edition)
Bailliere's Nurses' Medical Dictionary (1940)
Felicity Lawrence: *Additives: Your Complete Survival Guide* (Century Hutchinson Ltd.)
A. Scott Berg: *Charles Lindbergh*
Rev. Waddington Feather, poem on old age
Susan Glyn, poem on old age
Mrs C. Howell ('The Across Jumbo-Ambulance Experience')
Carol Steadman, Brecon Mountain Rescue team ('Mountain Rescues')
Eleanor Robbins ('Foster Parents')
Ann Vaughton ('The Good Samaritan and the Heart Operation')
Sue Pater ('Dr David Bellamy')
Gordon Chaldecott, Editor, *Merthyr Express*
The Public Library, Merthyr (for all the help given)
Christopher Allen alias Wood ('Homelessness')
Steve Booth, Tony and Karen, my dear neighbours who kept my laptop in order

Chapter 1

Disabled Not Discouraged

How precious is life? We accept it as a norm, except disabled children and people who struggle hard to prove their worth. This story is a tribute to all parents caring for a disabled child. In spite of the availability of termination for abnormal babies, many mothers will accept with love that little life stirring within.

Parents of disabled children will tell you of their deep love bond with these children. An ordinary factory worker told his mates: 'God is good, after years we are going to have a child.' The long awaited baby arrived, a 'Down's syndrome' child. When back at work one mate said sarcastically. 'So God gave you a Down's syndrome baby?' After a long silence the father answered slowly, 'Yes, and I'm glad he gave this child to me and not you.'

I feel the same about my son Robin, for whom I cared for 30 years. I am glad he came to me and no one else as I loved him from the start and knew I was capable caring for him.

When a vulnerable, damaged, helpless baby looks up at you, your protective instinct reaches out to guard, love and care for the child, no matter how many years lie ahead. An accepted disabled child comes with many blessings, more than the old saying, 'Every baby comes with a loaf of bread in its mouth'.

There is a moving story of the famous actress Elizabeth Taylor, who visited a Munich hospital in 1961 and heard a baby cry. It had been hidden by staff because it was crippled. She demanded to see the baby and seeing its disability said: 'I want that baby.' She arranged for it to have expensive corrective surgery and the baby grew up as one of their own, Elizabeth and Richard Burton's child.

Then there was Emma. When Susan Hill realised her just born

1

baby girl was a Down's syndrome child, she didn't want to know and left her in the hospital to be adopted. They called back: would she kindly continue breast feeding the baby for a little while, as she would not take the bottle. She went back and forth to the hospital and the nurses had to hold the little bundle against Susan, who refused even to hold the baby. One morning, waiting for the nurse, the baby cried and Susan instinctively picked her up. The baby cuddled to her and stopped crying, and a bond was sealed. Susan took the baby home and her other two children were delighted, helping to bath their little sister. Emma was accepted joyfully in the family. In fact the story goes on. Emma grew up surrounded and loved by her family, and she even joined a theatre company and eventually appeared in *The Bill*.

What about the ordinary widow in Cardigan where we lived in the 1980s. Her child, a complete vegetable, couldn't walk or talk and needed nursing constantly. She used to push this unfortunate child around in a pram, lovingly, and when it died was inconsolable. There had been a deep bond between them. Would this child have been able to communicate on a modern computer, as the following boy?

Rick Hoyt was a quadriplegic who couldn't speak. When he was born, doctors told his parents he would be a vegetable but they were determined to raise him like any other child. When he was ten, his life changed dramatically. Engineers at Tuffs School of Medicine in the USA created a device that enabled him to communicate via a computer. Up to then he had spent time sitting with the family watching television. They thought he was just sitting, unaware of what went on. But his first words on the computer were: 'Go Bruins!' (an American sports team). That's when everyone realised he was a sports fan. After a long battle with his computer, Rick got into public school, where he excelled. Two years later he took part in a 5-kilometre fund-raising race. His father pushed him in a modified wheelchair. In 1981 they ran the Boston Marathon. Since then they haven't missed a race. Rick has since earned his degree and works at Boston University helping design computer systems for people with disabilities (all with the help of a computer).

On 14th May 2003 there was a TV programme about Paula Sage, another Down's syndrome child who became a successful actress. And there are many more such cases, published or hidden.

This does not mean the ordinary, unheard of, Down's syndrome or any other disabled child is a useless burden. Nothing is further from the truth. No one knows the deep love and happiness these children give out. And whereas the parents should be recommended for caring for such a child, so should the Down's syndrome or other disabled child be recommended for the way they attempt to get on in spite of their disabilities, for they are the stars of heaven; they are the blessed of God.

Chapter 2

About Robin

Robin my son was born on 4th January 1956. He seemed normal, no fingers or toes missing. Yet we felt something was not quite right. We could not put our finger on it. The midwife assured us and said crudely: 'He's OK, ready to reproduce when grown up. He's got all the equipment!' But he did not develop at the same rate as my other three children. He didn't walk till nearly two. He had speech therapy at four years old, which helped. To our joy he was able to ride a three-wheeler bike at three and a fairy two-wheeler a year later. We paid for him to attend a private nursery school at four.

The first real symptom that all was not well was his skin, which would peel off and get soft and sore wherever two skin folds met. He also started wheezy attacks (asthma). So we took him to swimming lessons and would rush off to the Ilford pool weekly. Mrs Brown was his swimming teacher and strangely she was one of the 24-nurse set when I started to train at King's College hospital in 1942. She was then a swimming champion and after passing her nursing exams turned to work as a swimming instructor.

Robin did well and enjoyed swimming, and his wheezy attacks diminished when he was about ten years old. We managed to get him into an ordinary infant school at five years old and held our breath. Being very loveable and completely non-aggressive, he managed to hang on, but the headmistress warned me that he might have problems in the senior school. We carried on regardless, helping him at home with reading and arithmetic. He went to Cubs and even went camping with them. But again the leader, Akela, told us, the only reason he made it at camp was because they gave him much personal help.

4

Still we carried on, hoping he would eventually be all right. It illustrates the desperate attempts of many parents of disabled children to keep them in a normal school.

So what was Robin really like to make him apart from my other children? He was affectionate, eagerly trying to please, with times of clarity, but slow in conversation and behaviour; at other times his speech was confused. His problems did indeed start when he got to the senior school. There he was really out of his depth. He did have a special friend and even a girlfriend, which was ruined by the other boys. A sweet little letter from the girl was seized, ridiculed and torn up. He was bullied and teased. It went on until he became very disturbed and began to do odd things. The headmaster got in touch, telling us Robin's behaviour was strange. Of course nobody knew about the bullying till much later. Robin still, 30 years later, keeps saying: 'Why did they call me mental man?' He must have suffered agonies and not been able to talk or tell about it. One of the incidents was when some boys shook paint powder over him, and his blazer was completely covered. The school apologised and paid for the blazer to be cleaned, but the psychological damage must have been irreparable. This happened in the arts room, where Robin seemed to do well.

At that moment in time I had a friend whose son had become mentally ill. She told me how extremely good a certain professor was, who was renowned for having written several books on mental behaviour. So I took Robin to him for a consultation at the London hospital psychiatric unit. With hindsight I now realise that this was my biggest mistake, because he immediately diagnosed him as schizophrenic. The books he wrote were all on schizophrenia. Had we trusted our own doctor he might have come to a different conclusion; he knew Robin from birth, his slowness in thriving and progressing in speech, walking and all other activities of a child.

All these things, although mentioned in consultation, were brushed aside. We, his family and friends, some of whom are professionals, now know different and have come to the conclusion that Robin is autistic. Far be it from me to offend the learned profession, but mistakes have been made in every area of health matters. But at least the powers that be have relented and changed his diagnosis to partly autistic. The loyalty between consultants is too strong to ever waive an original diagnosis.

5

Chapter 3

Autism, as I Understand It

Chambers Dictionary describes autism as: 'absorption in imaginative activity directed by the thinker's wishes, with loss of contact with reality, an abnormality of childhood development affecting language and social communication'.

Autism is one of those mysteries. Whereas some autistic children are completely vague about their surroundings, others may have a brilliant streak.

There were three autistic children documented on television some years ago. One boy was taken to see St Paul's Cathedral in London. When back home, he drew the cathedral in absolutely perfect detail, every window in place, all from memory. It was found that he could draw anything from memory, yet otherwise he had to be cared for in a home.

The second boy could play anything he heard, from classical to modern music, on the piano. As all musicians know, practice is essential if you want to be accomplished. Yet this boy seemed to be able to play by ear. Again this was his only functional ability.

The third boy would be able to tell you the day your birthday would fall on many years ahead.

These three boys illustrate the mystery of the minds of some autistic children. It explains Robin's ability to hang on to a normal school up to senior grade. He could draw to perfection, his arithmetic was good, but otherwise he needed much help.

Robin went into the London Psychiatric Unit as a 5 foot 11 inch boy weighing 10 stone, he came home three months later weighing 14 stone and dribbling, not even knowing who he was, like a zombie. So much for the drugs they prescribed, and obviously his weight was not monitored. Within three months I had him back to 10 stone and less zombie-like. I believe that the psychiatric team go all out for the mental behaviour and pay little attention to physical condition. As for diet, bread and cakes were top of the menu. The moment bread and cakes were reduced, Robin started to lose weight. Could he be wheat sensitive? The schizophrenic society in Bangor claims it could be one of the conditions of schizophrenia (though we now think Robin is not schizophrenic but autistic).

My second oldest daughter, Patricia, married with two children, became seriously ill. Their father, who owned two shops in Norfolk, brought the two young children to me and I cared for them plus my disabled son Robin (then 15 years old). Having to care for my family meant I had to retire two years before my sixtieth birthday. I went house-hunting and bought my 100-year-old dream cottage in the Forest of Dean. So here we were, a little band of people, me, Robin, Michael, seven years old, and Melissa, two.

There were three buildings, a stable with upstairs room, probably to store hay, a smaller tool and workshop building and the cottage, all built in local traditional stone. The cottage had 10-inch thick walls and a heavy oak door with a huge equally thick and heavy key. We had a Swedish wood-burning stove installed as we were allowed to gather fallen wood from the forest quite freely. This stove was our pride and joy, and we spent much of our time collecting wood, barrowloads of it, then stacking the logs against the cottage wall, bringing them in, laying them beside the burning stove to dry, ready to be used. All this enthusiastic work for feeding our hungry, warmth-giving stove, which heated the whole cottage upstairs and downstairs.

At the back of the cottage was a stone patio with a 100-foot-deep well. We were told it had been dug during a miners' strike years ago by the then owner. The well was surrounded by a 2-foot ornamental brick wall with traditional small roof over it which was supported by two pillars on either side, and underneath a pail hanging on a rope ready to draw water. The water in the well was pure and sweet and in any drought there was plenty available. The garden was 200 feet long and approximately 40 feet wide, first a patio, then a fair-sized lawn, followed by a vegetable garden, and lastly at the bottom a small orchard with apple and pear trees. The path leading down the garden by the boundary side had blackcurrants, redcurrants and gooseberry bushes. I brought three beehives with me from Chigwell (my hobby the last year before moving). Placing them in the middle of the orchard seemed ideal and the bees appeared to be happy. So with our vegetable garden, berry bushes, orchard and honeybees, we were practically self-supporting. My two grandchildren and Robin adored the Forest of Dean with its hidden mysteries and adventures. Apart from our own produce, the forest and surrounding land yielded wild strawberries, damsons and real chestnuts. In the small village of Bream, a mile from us, were three large walnut trees and in the right season we would gather field mushrooms at the crack of dawn.

Chapter 4

Robin and Allergies

In the Forest of Dean, Robin started to have bizarre attacks, completely alien to his usual gentle self. He was on medication as prescribed at the London hospital. The sort of things he would do would happen suddenly, out of the blue. He would break a cup or pull the curtains down or bang his head against a wall. He did none of these things prior to being given the medication for mental behaviour. Once he did an 'Incredible Hulk' act by running out of the cottage onto the green where boys played football, tearing one goal post out of the ground in front of the amazed boys, and flinging it aside. He returned to the cottage, went up to his room and lay on the bed. I rushed out, embarrassed, to replace the goal post. The boys wouldn't let me and said, good humouredly, 'Don't worry, Mrs Wood, we'll do it.' They understood Robin's condition. When I asked Robin why he did this, he said: 'I felt unwell.'

There was another serious, if not funny, incident. He went off on his bike, leaving the designated area, and did not return. None of the neighbours had seen him. The worry was terrible. Six hours later the police from the main M4 observation centre phoned. 'Have you a son called Robin? Good, come and collect him.' I raced to the police centre (approximately 20 miles), where I was told several motorists had phoned them to say that a boy was cycling down the M4. They sent a patrol car to apprehend him, but alas every time the police car reached him and stopped, and the policeman got out of the patrol car, taking out notebook and pen ... Robin just cycled round him and raced off again shouting, 'I'm going to Chigwell.' It eventually took three patrol cars surrounding him to stop him. Of course when they tried to question him, he made no sense, and they realised his disturbance. The only lucid thing he

9

said was, 'I want to go to Chigwell.' They asked him where in Chigwell and he knew our old address. I gather they sent a Chigwell policeman there to inquire, and of course the new owners knew about Robin and our new address in the Forest of Dean, which enabled the police to contact me. When I arrived at the police centre, Robin was sitting there happily eating a sandwich and having a cup of tea. The police told me they had taken the back wheel off the bike and advised me to keep it off so that Robin wouldn't be able to ride off again. No charges were made. I duly took Robin home, plus the dismantled bike, which was put into the workshop.

This wasn't the end of the story as a week later Robin disappeared into the workshop and came out, bike assembled, and moved off again. By the time I found my car keys to follow him, he was out of sight. Fortunately for him, he had it badly assembled and the back wheel came off a mile down the road. A kind neighbour happened to come by in his van and brought him back, bike, wheel and all. I now hid the wheel in a neighbour's shed, where it must be to this day, though he did get another bike years later. Robin's distorted behaviour was a great worry to me, especially as I had my two grandchildren to care for as well, though Michael was at school most of the time. Of course they both thought Robin's behaviour hilarious.

I started to read everything I could get hold of to do with mental behaviour. At that time a book came on the market called *Not All in the Mind* by Dr Richard Mackarness, a psychiatric consultant at Basingstoke hospital. He claimed he could improve or even cure some mental conditions by eliminating allergy-causing foods. I immediately followed his advice and put Robin on what he called a cave man's diet. This consisted of only home-cooked meat, vegetables and fruit for a week, then I introduced other foods slowly, one at a time, keeping records of reactions. If it caused a disturbance, then I eliminated it altogether from the diet, as this was an allergic reaction. I kept a diary for three months and a pattern emerged. There was no doubt Robin was allergic to additives in foods. Sadly, some of his favourite things, like ice cream, flavoured crisps and sweets, were laced with additives. Also anything containing monosodium glutamate, which is in many processed foods, would send him sky high. The moment he stopped having these foods he became again the gentle, slow, confused Robin. One mistake on my part by giving him something with additives and we would have to pay the price of disturbance.

With this controlled diet, Robin was now manageable and we seemed to be living a happy, normal life exploring the lovely Forest of Dean and taking the children back and forth to school. Five years passed and my daughter was still in and out of hospital down in Kent near her father. Her marriage had broken down and a divorce took place. Lawrence, the children's father, married again and wanted his son. I knew it was right. Michael having passed his 11 plus exam was now out of my league as regards helping him with his homework. He had a strong bond with his father, who had visited him almost weekly from Norfolk right down the long way to the Forest of Dean. Melissa followed her brother a year later. Now there was only Robin and me. I started a voluntary car service, taking disabled people back and forth to evening socials. This was very convenient as of course it included Robin and me being there at the gathering to enjoy the fun. There was a young social worker who arranged most of the socials. He was so very charming and kind. Everybody liked him, especially the disabled youngsters. These socials sometimes went on till 10 p.m. There was a disabled young chap living right the other side of Gloucester, not on my route, and his parents used to bring him in. The social worker offered to put the young man up overnight in his flat to save the parents the late journey. He would bring him for occupational therapy the next morning and the usual transport would take him back.

Alas, a rumour circulated, the social worker was arrested, tried and jailed for six months. I never found out if it was abuse or rape the disabled young man suffered. This was in the 1980s and I often wondered if this social worker was cured or, now in his fifties, if he is still a danger to the community, as paedophile registers did not exist then. It illustrates the danger disabled people may be in when tended by unchecked staff, which happily now is against the law.

Chapter 5

Friends of Oak House

At this time I met Mr and Mrs Gough at a parents' meeting for disabled children and young adults. They were remarkable people, having bought a large three-storey country house a few miles out of Coleford, Gloucester, and turned it into a home for disabled boys and young adults. They offered themselves as mother and father to these unfortunate boys and loved them and were loved by them.

I joined their league of friends (Friends of Oak House) and spent many happy hours (with Robin) at Oak House, helping with outings, leisure activities and festivities. Oak House was run very efficiently, with residents engaged in work, leisure, hobbies and outings. Yes, even dancing! I remember one dance we took them to; the boys were formally dressed with bow ties. The boys able to walk would come to your chair, bow and ask you politely (all Mrs Gough's training) to dance, even if their speech happened to be impaired. After the dance, they would escort you back to your seat and say 'Thank you'. Most of them had two left feet for dancing, as the saying goes, but nevertheless enjoyed the movement and the holding of a partner. The immobile chaps would equally enjoy just sitting, watching, swaying to the music or tapping to the rhythm.

Mrs Gough, besides being a very efficient mother and organiser, was an artist, her drawings life-like. She used to encourage the boys to draw and make all kinds of pictures, baskets and other ornamental and useful items. The yearly open day would be quite an event, displaying the boys' works of arts and crafts. Coffee, tea and refreshments were served by the boys. Robin and I usually spent the day there with the other friends of Oak House.

Christmas, birthdays and other festivities would always be

celebrated in style with presents for all concerned. I believe they took the boys once a year to the seaside. And of course day outings during the year and dinners out were numerous. Dinner parties were held frequently and the way these boys behaved was remarkable; their manners were excellent, again thanks to Mrs Gough's training.

I remember one day above the others. We took them by minibus to Worcester by the river Severn on a glorious sunny day. There was a fair with rides, bumper cars and all the other traditional amusements. How these boys enjoyed the simple rides made one's heart glad.

In the week the boys would sometimes be taken to do gardening projects in the district. Many times they came to me to do gardening and enjoyed hot chocolate and doughnuts at break time. They loved coming to our garden, which helped me a great deal.

I remained friends with Oak House long after we moved, but sadly Mr and Mrs Gough are now dead and I believe their adopted son took over. My memory of Oak House is one of 16 gentle, smiling boys trying hard to please, very much like Robin.

Robin always showed a slight reluctance at Oak House. I believe he already knew that sometime he might have to go to a place like this. I think he had an inner kind of foreboding, whereas I still felt that I had years ahead with Robin at home.

Chapter 6

Music and Kittens

Now with the children gone there was an empty void. We missed them dearly. So I decided to learn to play the guitar, then teach Robin, who loved music. We found a teacher in Monmouth and both Robin and I enjoyed the first classical tunes, then chords. Robin seemed to learn quickly in spite of his slowness and disability.

The drive to Monmouth was fantastic, especially in winter when snowflakes drifted across my windscreen, illuminated fairylike by light beams from high up on lampposts when coming down the mountain. We had so much fun with our music; Robin could sing simple tunes, like 'Cockles and mussels a-live-a-live-o...' He also had a good voice, especially in church, singing hymns.

Now at that time I began to feel the garden was hard work even with the help of the Oak House boys. No sooner had I finished tending down at the bottom 200 feet away, than the top shrieked out for my renewed attention. Now nearing 70 years old, I felt the strain. It became too much for me and I decided to buy a place with a smaller garden. Searching for properties was fun with Robin by my side, with his excellent navigating and road-sign reading. We drove from the Forest of Dean to Cornwall, Devon and Wales. We saw properties advertised as 'by a bubbling brook' – a dirty, smelly backwater; with 'panoramic views' – miles up a mountain to nowhere up a stony track; and 'needs attention' – a place that was falling down. Eventually we found a delightful cottage near Cardigan Bay in a small village called Llechryd, 5 miles from Cardigan. Again it had thick stone walls and was 100 years old. It had belonged to a vet, who used it as a holiday home. The small garden was charming, with a small plot down the road for growing vegetables and strawberries. There were only three cottages on this half-mile road.

So here we were, Robin and I, with one golden Labrador and two cats, one a Siamese kitten and the other a black and white cat. All these we loved. They had a special link with Robin as animals and disabled people seem to love each other in an understanding way. Sadly we lost all these three; they were poisoned as the farmers put cyanide in the fields to kill moles and rats. I wonder if these farmers have any clue how terribly a poisoned animal suffers before dying. I stayed with my Siamese cat and suffered with her. When the golden Labrador was afflicted in the same way, I rushed him to the vet, who gave him an injection to ease this awful death. Through the vet we complained about this dreadful practice and I think the farmers were told. We again rescued another dog from a dogs' home, this time a golden retriever, who lived to an old age and was loved by Robin and me.

In a shop window an advert stated 'Kitten needs home, apply within', so we did. The kitten apparently had been found at the back of a garden in Molygrove, a lovely little village. It was a wild little thing and we gave it a special place under the sink in the kitchen with a curtain cover, where it hid and only came out for food. After a while it became more confident and would use its sharp claws to dig into my legs and run up my jeans to where its food was being prepared. We called her Sarah. She had gorgeous long fur and lovely large eyes, a tabby cat. We loved her to bits and when she was a year old she had a litter of five kittens before being spayed. The kittens were lovely. Two were black, one tabby and one black with a funny streak across her nose we called 'Ugly'. She went to a farm and the others to good homes, except the last kitten, which was ginger. She looked so strange and light amongst the other dark kittens, so different; we just had to keep her.

Sarah was a wonderful mother, quite a story by itself. We had a shed with a stable door down the garden. I thought that to be the best place for Sarah to have her kittens, so we prepared a nice bed for her and waited the arrival of our little brood. She did use the shed. It was a very hot day and the top of the stable door was open for air. It must have been too hot for the kittens and when we went down to look at them, she had laid them all out separately in a row. My daughter Pat, who was down for a visit, said: 'Don't touch them, Mum, she'll deal with them.' We waited inside the cottage and, would you believe it? she picked them up one at a time and brought them all into the cottage, past us and up the

15

stairs to safety to the bathroom. She knew that the shed was too hot and they would surely have died. What a mother, and how gently she held them by their necks and carried them to safety. This wasn't the end of the story, because we were going upstairs to the toilet, and pulling the chain wasn't acceptable to Sarah, so there was another move of her little family. She brought them all down again one by one and hid them behind the TV set.

This lovely pet lived to be 18 years old. Years later while Robin was in hospital, now in Merthyr Tydfil, she became so ill she could hardly walk and weighed only a few ounces. I knew her time had come; she was in pain and the kindest thing was to let her go to sleep. As the vet could not help her any more, I called him to the cottage rather than take her to the surgery; I felt I owed her that much. I had her on my lap, asleep, when he came. He gave her an injection while she was asleep on my lap and she went into a permanent sleep and I held her lovingly for another half-hour with tears falling into her lovely long silky fur. I then put her just as she was, curled up, into one of the round flower baskets that my children had given me, filled with flowers, for a birthday.

My good neighbours Lisa and Mark Thomas buried her in the basket, up the mountain behind our house where she loved to roam. I could not go with them but watched from my window as they did the honours. Mark walked ahead with a spade, followed by Lisa carrying the basket like something precious, and finally Kylie, their nine-year-old son, bringing up the rear. Eighteen years of loyal love and companionship buried on a Welsh mountain.

Ginger followed her next year, also aged 18.

Chapter 7

Water Sport, Art and Snooker

Back to Llechryd. This little village and the surrounding area, from Carmarthen up to Bangor, offered an unbelievable amount of facilities: a social club, canoeing, windsurfing at Goodwick, swimming at Newcastle Emlyn 3 miles away, and many church outings and family do's. There were marquetry sessions further up the coast near Aberayron for retired folk, occupational therapy for Robin at Newcastle Emlyn, not to forget the lovely Pembrokeshire coast and the scenery up to Snowdon. The village itself had a spacious hall for jumble sales, church do's and badminton once a week. I enrolled Robin and myself straight away to play badminton. Since we had paid for Robin for tennis lessons when we lived in Chigwell, he was excellent at badminton and surprised the locals by his sometimes hilarious winning shots. Being nearly 6 foot tall, he would stretch out his arms and catch the shuttle at the tip of his racket without moving, while the rest of the players were rushing all over the court. Robin was well liked in spite of his sometimes confused talk. We were always given the first few games as they realised Robin got tired easily. The kindness of these people was terrific and besides the release of tension for Robin, it made him feel proud that he belonged a little, if not completely.

At Goodwick, windsurfing lessons were available and we were brave enough to try this water sport. We went in threes, my daughter Patricia, Robin and me. I must confess that on the surf board, splashing backwards into the water was my fate, to the amusement of any onlookers, whereas Robin was the only one able to balance, stay, yes and even move. This again illustrates his autism. He had no fear; he just seemed to give in to the surf board and the way the waves rolled. After each surfing lesson we would be allowed

17

to canoe around the bay. This too was very exhilarating and Robin seemed to be the most efficient, though Patricia and I enjoyed it as well. The surfing lessons and canoeing were always topped by having tea in the Fishguard Harbour café, watching the Irish ferry filling with passengers and cars, then sailing off.

We had very few windsurfing lessons, as we did not seem to progress. Anyway, there were other sports facilities we could enjoy. We all three went horse riding with the disabled. We would just sit on the horse and in company with other disabled people trot through lovely country lanes, through woods and besides little babbling brooks. All this for Robin's sake and he certainly enjoyed it.

Long before we moved, way back in Chigwell, Robin had loved painting. He painted in oils and Japanese pastels. I have his paintings hanging all over the house and sadly gave many away to relatives. So when we found out that an arts club existed right on our doorstep in Cardigan, I enrolled Robin straight away and we had many happy days in the countryside with easel, chairs and paints, sitting in the company of other enthusiasts by little streams and sandy beaches whose waves rolled in, Robin painting and loving it, with me just sitting beside him watching.

At Christmas the club gave an exhibition of work accomplished. Robin entered (or I did for him) three paintings, one of Cenarth Falls (in oil) and two in Japanese pastels. Cenarth Falls was sold the first week, to my joy, but Robin did not seem to take in the importance of his painting with his name on it being displayed in someone's house – another sign of his autism. Only a few paintings were sold and when we went to collect the remaining two, there was only one left of Robin's, so another had been sold. It was a tree by a stream in Japanese pastels. My joy was boundless, yet Robin was unmoved; he could not comprehend or feel joy, yet while painting he seemed relaxed and his usual tension was gone.

The Gateway social club, where he went without me, being collected and brought back, had sports facilities. There was table tennis, billiards, snooker, and a table where games could be played. Tea and refreshments were available. Once a month, families could join and socialise with each other. Table tennis was Robin's favourite and he beat almost everyone. What impressed me was the way some of the very disturbed, maybe autistic, young men would play snooker. Obviously they had watched this game on TV, and observed it in every detail in regard to position, lowered head, eyes on ball, concentrating on the cue line to ball. They would stand exactly like an accomplished player, straight back bent from the hips to straight upright legs at 90 degrees, in a corner position, rigid, concentrating, cue pointing directly to the ball. This illustrates that autistic people can take in what they see and even express it; but it also shows the restricted capabilities of the autistic person: the way they take in what they see is like computers.

Chapter 8

The Sex Therapist

Parents of disabled children will understand my frantic everlasting search to improve Robin's condition. Anything, anything, clutching at straws. Mothers have been doing it going back in history. Even the Russian Tsarina back in the 1900s whose son suffered from haemophilia (absence of normal blood clotting agents which could prove fatal with even the slightest cut) entrusted her little son and family, even state secrets, to the infamous, uncouth, womaniser Rasputin with his long black unkempt beard. All because he had a calming influence on the sick little Tsarevich. His disastrous hold on the family and his bad advice helped the downfall and murder by revolutionaries of the whole royal family and even the sick little Tsarevich in 1918. A mother's love will go to unbelievable lengths if she thinks help is at hand, even if it is against other professional advice. The child's good health seems to be of the ultimate importance. I'm afraid I am just as anxious for Robin's improvement if it is at all possible.

I saw an advertisement in the local press for a 'nature therapist' in our own locality. I went for it even though in the 1980s most general practitioners still looked at alternative medicine with suspicion, and even animosity. Apparently this person was a sex therapist, but I did not know then about the sex bit, though it seems everybody else did. He had a cottage up a small mountain a mile out of town, and I took Robin there for a consultation. The therapist looked at us for a long moment trying to assess where we fitted in. After my explanation of Robin's problems and my hopes of a cure, he said he couldn't promise to restore Robin to normality, but thought relaxation sessions might help. We went weekly for nearly a year at £8 a time. Robin seemed to enjoy it and always looked forward to his treatment. I think any person-to-person contact is pleasing to a disabled person, anything where time and effort is spent on their behalf.

Out of these sessions came two important results. The first, not so good: not knowing about the sex bit, in my naivety, I told all and sundry about my visit with Robin to this therapist, which caused raised eyebrows and left me wondering and puzzling. This led us to no end of embarrassment later on. The second, good: because the therapist was a qualified doctor and had time on his hands, unlike a general practitioner who has so many patients. He told us that the charity organisation Across, which organised jumbo-ambulance holidays for the disabled, had asked him to be the doctor on one of their trips. He in turn asked me as a trained nurse to come and bring Robin as a disabled person.

This holiday for disabled people was going to take place a month later, giving us plenty of time to get organised. In the meantime there were several exciting events coming up in Cardigan for Robin and me to take part in.

Chapter 9

Exploring Wales

My daughter, now recovered from her illness, followed me to Llechryd and met and married a Welshman, Dennis Jones. At weekends they joined Robin and me touring Wales, from the gorgeous three Tenby beaches to Snowdon in North Wales, sampling on the way the Centre for Alternative Technology. Built, I believe, in 1980, it was the first to have solar panels and other self-supporting natural means. Their windmills could be seen miles before reaching the centre. Then there was the interesting craft centre near Coris with its hexagonal art buildings displaying many Welsh crafts, and a Welsh kitchen and coffee shop with delicious home-cooked Welsh food.

Later, driving to Portmadoc, we passed the (sixpenny, then) toll, then onto the narrow pass with the fantastic view, mountains on one side and the sea on the other. All these routes Robin navigated, reading the signs and giving directions, with Patricia and Dennis sitting in the back of the car. Robin felt in charge in this very important position of trust. He reads well but when reading books does not seem to take in their content except very easy children's first reading books. This is another condition of autism. Reading was one of the things we did with him when young. For instance, he reads anything to do with space and stars. He'll be able to understand how many light years away in numbers from the earth the planets are, but cannot comprehend a novel.

We stayed at a youth hostel a couple of miles outside Beddgelert, above a deep blue lake. Beddgelert is famous for the dog that saved a baby from a wolf and got shot by his master by mistake. He thought that the dog had attacked the baby, but later found the dead wolf. It had been the wolf's blood on the dog's jaw, from their fight. There is a small memorial for 'The Dog of Beddgelert'.

In the youth hostel, Robin helped with cooking, making up his own bunk and other menial tasks. The other youth hostellers liked Robin and tolerated his odd ways and sometime strange conversation. We climbed Watkins Path, Robin and Dennis bringing rucksacks with picnics, but did not quite make the top, as the last yards were slimy, slippery and dangerous. We compensated by taking the train next day in Llanberis, which took us to the summit minus sweat and effort.

We got to know North Wales extensively, including the fantastic waterfall at Betws-y-Coed and the lovely lake at Bala.

They were happy days, but on reaching my seventies that silent nagging feeling 'What will happen to Robin if anything happens to me?' kept rising. This must happen to all parents who care for their disabled children and the prospect of this event becomes a nightmare.

Chapter 10

The Swiss Journey

In 1981 we received an invitation to stay with my nephew in Switzerland. I decided to drive and spend one night in a youth hostel to break the journey. I was then 63 years old and Robin 35. He was excellent as a passenger and a very helpful navigator. In spite of his confusion and disability he knew how to read road signs. I knew we would manage between the two of us. I booked with the AA and with a very helpful driving plan, set off.

To begin with, we stayed with Robin's dad in Kent, near Sevenoaks, then took the ferry to Zeebrugge. All very exciting. The boat had a swimming pool, which we both sampled. Large waves billowed up and down in unison with the boat's movement on the Channel waves. We browsed through the ship's shop and wandered the upper deck, enjoyed the food in the restaurant and relaxed in the lavish rest rooms. After disembarking we drove through Belgium, then onto the German autobahn, which had apparently been built during Hitler's regime. It was constructed in an absolute straight line, cutting through everything in its way. On this autobahn you could see miles and miles ahead, no curves, no corners. The youth hostel we stayed in was superb, built all in pinewood. All German youth hostels are built tastefully. Then on to Basel, only ten miles from my nephew.

Alfred and his wife Gerda have an architect-designed, modern chalet-type house half way up a mountain overlooking the river Rhine and Germany on the other side. An ancient covered wooden bridge led to Säckingen, a German town where we spent many mornings sampling German cakes and coffee. We had a fabulous time, being taken all over Switzerland to beauty spots, up snowy mountains so high they were near to the top of the world, and one

24

of the deepest and narrowest gorges, the Aare Schlucht, fantastic, awesome, something to be seen, between two mountains, deep down, its gurgling river winding through. Great steel girders had been cut into the rock face on one side to carry a small path. We all held onto the steel rails with bated breath, looking down into the seeming abyss. How could man build this? A feat of workmanship. Did Robin really appreciate all this, would he remember, in later life? I don't know. My Swiss-German-speaking relations took his confused talk as normal. Their English was somewhat worse than Robin's double-dutch. So everybody was happy. I would make up something on Robin's behalf to my satisfaction. We returned home very satisfied and happy, having spent a glorious two weeks amongst our Swiss relations.

Chapter 11

Foster Parents

There are many stories of these unsung heroes who open their homes and hearts to thousands of children, neglected, abused or abandoned by their own, disabled or from broken or violent homes, many disturbed and orphaned, some mere babies. Some provide short-term care, while mothers are in hospital or for other family problems, but fostering is mainly long-term care lasting years, till the children are grown up. They become loving substitute parents for their charges. They treat them as their own, support them, and make them feel important. They go with them to the first day at a strange school for support, help with homework, give birthday parties, attend school functions, and help in all those things a parent would do to give a child confidence to get adjusted to society.

There was a report of American foster parents who looked after 13 children, all a happy family together. Apparently three washing machines were on the go daily. The food intake was on a scale like a delivery to a small food shop, their house like a small hotel and their transport a bus. There was a cupboard full of medication, preventatives and cures for colds and other minor upsets. Holidays and outings were arranged like a coach tour outing, and festive days became a major celebration. This is an outstanding family, as mostly foster parents will foster two–three children.

Sometimes, sadly, after having cared for a child for a long time and loving that child, they will have to give it back to an estranged parent now demanding its return, maybe having found a new partner, or financial matters having improved. This is often done through the law. This is very heartbreaking and traumatic for both child and foster parents, but it does happen. To avoid this, some foster parents have adopted their foster children after caring for them for years.

Foster parents do a wonderful job, filling the gap for unwanted children. The State pays them for each child; I call it board and lodging, as dedication and love cannot be bought.

We were lucky to meet such a family at the Gateway club for the disabled, at a monthly parent get-together. We became great friends with the Robbins, typical foster parents, who owned a very large house with extensive grounds in Sarnau, only ten minutes from Penbryn beach, which is perfect for swimming. They owned two horses which needed daily riding for exercise. So riding and swimming were on the menu. What a place for boys to grow up in! The Robbins were loving parents to three boys, all from different backgrounds. Each one had either a slight physical or mental disability. The oldest, Reno, was a gentle, slow, tall boy, then came Garry, who had a walking impediment, and Jason, the youngest, only five years old, seemed disturbed and quite a handful to manage.

Robin and I were always welcome there and spent many happy hours in their company, including having fun by the sea, swimming, playing games and having meals with them. We saw these boys growing up during our 12 years in Llechryd. Garry married and had two children, Reno was still there and Jason eventually went to another home. This was between 1979 and 1991, when we moved to Merthyr Tydfil, but we are still in touch after all these years.

Chapter 12

Thunder, Lightning and Death on the Beach

It was one of those hot sunny summer days. We decided to go to Poppitt Sands for the day. We loaded the car with picnic, towels and swimwear. Pat, Dennis, Robin and I made up the group. On the way, someone suggested we see the seals first, further up the coast, where we could also see Cardigan Island, a bird sanctuary. We drove to Gwbert-on-Sea and parked in the Gwbert hotel car park. It was less than a mile's walk to where we hoped to see the seals. We were lucky, they were out in force, some sunning themselves lying way below us on the rocks, others sliding in and out of the sea. Their antics were well worth our walk. Did they know we were watching them? Was their frolicking meant just for us or was it just their normal behaviour? Whatever, we enjoyed just watching them.

Quite suddenly the atmosphere around us changed, as if a thick black blanket had been pulled over the whole sky. Without warning, cracking thunder erupted and struck into our ears and lightning zigzagged around us like dancing, in front and behind us. Fear gripping all of us, we only thought of getting back to the (hopeful) safety of the car, frantically holding and gripping each other, stumbling, running, terror-stricken, the less than a mile to the car which seemed endlessly far. We were only half way back to the car when the lightning stopped, but the most heavy deluge followed. It simply poured buckets. We were all soaked to the skin.

We could hear police and ambulance sirens in the distance and then could see the vehicles across the bay at Poppitt Sands. We got to the car looking dishevelled, hair hanging over our faces, wet clothes clinging to our bodies and shoes carried in our hands as wetness made them slippery. Running barefoot over stones and

28

rocks had made our feet sore and bruised. Shaken and trembling we scrambled into the car and drove back to Dennis's house, where his parents, shocked at our state, helped us to dry off and gave us some clean dry clothing and a hot cup of tea.

We found out that at Poppitt Sands, the moment the black cloud appeared, the lifeguards through loudspeakers ordered 'Clear the beach... Clear the beach...' Apparently the beach, which had been absolutely crowded with families playing games and swimming in the sea, was empty within 15 minutes, everybody grabbing their belongings and rushing back to the safety of their cars. One man who was running was killed by lightning in front of his family. Hence the police and ambulance, which were there at the scene within minutes. The media carried this tragic story all the next day.

I still try to remember which of us made us change our minds and go to the seals first, before going to Poppitt Sands, and so avoid a great danger that day.

Chapter 13

Celebrations, Festivities and Coracle Races

Cenarth waterfall is one of the highlights on the Carmarthen to Cardigan road. The huge waterwheel next to the old mill is still working. On the other side of the falls over the ancient bridge, a coffee shop overlooks the falls, with a souvenir shop. And there are parking facilities right down by the waterfall.

Many times Robin and I watched with fascination the salmon leaping up the fantastic river Teifi waterfall from Cenarth Bridge, while on the other side in calm waters a coracle or two were navigating.

I understand from the locals that these strange black oval-shaped small craft (about 6 feet long and 2 feet wide) were hanging by every cottage door in Cenarth way back hundreds of years ago, but now only one remains, by the little pub opposite the entrance to the water wheel.

In Llechryd there still resided a coracle craftsman. Mr Thomas's house on the main Carmarthen to Cardigan road lay back approximately 4 yards from the road, separated by a strip of grassland. There were always three shiny black tar-covered coracles resting on the strip: one completely finished, one half-finished and one at the beginning of construction. Mr Thomas was one of the few left who knew about this ancient craft. He gave lectures to schools and meetings etc.

From my understanding, a coracle was made up basically of ash trees cut into lashes for the frame, then covered in canvas and secured with cow's tail rope and finished off with black waterproofing tar. Only one man can sit in it and with a 10-pound salmon would fill the boat. Usually it takes two coracles to fish, and between them they pull a net along the riverbed. Of course if they net a 10-pound salmon, that would feed a family more than once.

A coracle is very difficult to enter and manoeuvre. It can capsize easily and strangers trying to get in often land in the water, to the coracle man's delight. The coracle man knows his art and how to use this wobbly little boat. Robin was not afraid of being taken for a ride by a coracle man and he enjoyed the sensation. I was happy to just watch.

One of the strangest sights is to see two coracle-carrying men walking towards you side by side. With their coracles hanging over their heads and covering their backs like a half-opened shell, exposing only their feet, they appear like two giant walking beetles.

The yearly coracle races from Cilgerran down the river Teifi were a spectacle not to be missed.

Crowds cheered them on their way to Cardigan, where the pubs were ready to serve the crews. Apart from the coracle races there were usually other events to mark the day and delight the crowds assembled there waiting, such as the raft race. This featured home-made affairs, usually badly assembled floating paraphernalia which often came apart mid-stream, leaving a desperate crew swimming around trying to catch and save floating pieces of their precious masterpieces.

Then there was the rope across the river, attached securely either side to a lorry, inviting young enthusiasts to cross the river by dragging themselves across by laying their chest on the rope and pulling themselves across using outstretched arms. Many fell in even before they got half way and were picked up by the waiting boat. Some made it a little further and on one occasion only one man got all the way across.

I was told afterwards the poor young man was very sore, with a grazed line across his chest where the rope had rubbed, but the first prize, a salmon, consoled him for his agony.

Then there was the farmer's event with shire horses, ploughs and other farmers' equipment, parading down the main street of Cardigan, the horses, having been groomed especially for this event, proudly displaying ribbons won in previous events.

There were many more events, like the duck race. I never found out what this was but apparently it was very popular, with prizes and plenty of encouragement from the Cardigan crowd.

Lastly there was the Flying Beauty Queen event. The Beauty Queen would jump from the bridge with home-made wings to fly away with, but of course she landed in the drink and would have to be rescued by eager young suitors in their boats, who would carry her off. Robin was really concerned about the Beauty Queen until she was safely rescued and in the boat.

Chapter 14

The Across Trust Jumbo-Ambulance Experience

Before recounting our experience of the Across Trust Jumbo-Ambulance I must pay tribute to a little girl, Angie (Angela) O'Connor, who died in March 1976. She was one of hundreds of children suffering from the terrible illness cystic fibrosis and had to endure the four times a day pummelling of chest and back to vibrate and loosen the fluid and mucus which collects in the lungs – exhausting for the therapist but far more exhausting for the poor affected child. In spite of her painful illness she is reported to have been brave, understanding human suffering, still with some gaiety and having a mischievous smile. This is her description of her journeys to Lourdes with Jumbo-Ambulance:

> We sang songs together. We felt like a big family. All the people I have met through Jumbo-Ambulance are like brothers and sisters to me. I love them; I don't just look upon them as good friends because they mean more than that to me. As the time got near for us to go home, I felt sad, I was looking forward to going home again but I felt sad that we had to leave Lourdes behind us, but we didn't really, we brought Lourdes back in our memories.

Angie went four times to Lourdes. One day she told her mother, in her quiet and matter-of-fact way, that her time was near. On the morning of Wednesday 10th March 1976, with her mother and her friend Father Steward at her side, Angie died. She was buried in the little County Cemetery of Our Lady Queen of Heaven, North Chailey, Sussex, the parish church shared by the Anglican Community

33

and Catholic handicapped children who reside in the special home and school nearby. Her name is written in the visitors book dated 11th December 1975, the day after the feast of the Immaculate Conception.

The Across Trust Jumbo-Ambulance charity was started by Dick Glitheroe nearly 20 years ago. It sadly went into liquidation in 1996 due to lack of funds. The first Jumbo-Ambulance was a standard size. It had berths, a loo, a kitchen at the back and a hydraulic lift for wheelchairs. Then there was the double Jumbo-Ambulance called the Alligator (60 feet long, just like an articulated lorry). It could take 14 disabled people, 14 carers/helpers, a doctor, 2 nurses, 2 drivers, a group leader and sometimes a priest.

Carolyn Howells was an organiser from Milford Haven, Dyfed. She had the tremendous task of assembling disabled people, their carers and helpers, doctors and nurses, arranging journeys, stops for breaks, places to stay, hotels etc., and the end destination of the Jumbo-Ambulance holiday, then the return journey and the handing over of the disabled people to waiting relatives. Carolyn Howells is one of those wonderful people engaged in aiding disabled and sick people to achieve the chance of going on an exciting journey to a holiday abroad. Her trips with Jumbo-Ambulance included Austria, Germany, and Rome. On the Rome trip they even had an audience with the Pope. They went yearly to Lourdes and in the early days to Switzerland. Only the standard-size Jumbo-Ambulance went to Switzerland, the Alligator was too long to negotiate the winding mountain roads.

Robin and I went by Jumbo-Ambulance to Montana Vermala, Switzerland and stayed at a monastery, being served by monks. Montana is a small ski resort in the Bernese Alps surrounded by snow-bedecked mountains, a fabulous place. Skiers and people wrapped in furs were everywhere. The shops were full of top-priced gear, way out of our price range. Coffee and cakes were very expensive too, but oh so delicious. We trouped through the little town, pushing wheelchairs and walking the disabled, exploring shops and restaurants. The highlight of our stay was a ride on the mountain cable car taking us right up to the summit of Monte Rosa Mountain. We sat with bated breath looking deep down, hanging in mid-air saying a silent trembling prayer till safely at the top and on terra firma, then being awed by the fantastic view around us, mountains of ice and snow, the top of the world. Some

34

of the disabled had never been abroad, let alone on a high mountain in Switzerland. The weather too was on our side, sunshine every day, yet the snow did not melt and the skiers were not disappointed. We all, including Robin and myself, truly had a wonderful time in Montana and returned full of happy memories.

Chapter 15

The Thalidomide Tragedy

Chambers Dictionary states: '**thalidomide** is a non-barbiturate sedative drug, withdrawn in 1961 because found to cause malformation in the fetus if taken during pregnancy.'

Behind this short sentence lies hidden drama, shock and devastation for we don't know how many children's and parents' lives. These unfortunate deformed children are now grown up, some into clever people with handsome faces. Many have been given artificial limbs. However, as useful and helpful an artificial limb may be, it will never be the same as the one nature provides.

Going back to the 1950s, when this drug came onto the market, imagine the woman for whom it was prescribed. Imagine the nursery prepared with pretty cot draped with frilly lace, little teddy bears and all the other needs of the long-awaited baby. Perhaps it is a first baby, or maybe there are already some children, looking forward excitedly to their new baby sister or brother.

The day of birth arrives at last. Mother is rushed to hospital. Midwife and other staff are in attendance, including the husband giving support to his wife. The young mother is in labour for several hours. Imagine the effort, the pain, sweat and finally the last push. She hears the baby cry, which always thrills all in attendance. She relaxes with a deep sigh of contentment, the baby is born, it is alive, it breathes, the discomfort and pain are finally gone. She eagerly waits to receive her little bundle into her arms.

But there is an ominous stunned silence. The joy of those in attendance turns to shock. The baby has no arms, only two flipper-like hands growing straight from the sides of the chest.

The attending father breaks down. The nurses whisk the baby

36

away. Staff huddle together. How to explain this devastating fact to the now panicking mother? After getting over the first shock the mother has to be told, she will have to feed the baby. Now she and her husband cling together in fearful sorrow. 'Why...? Why...? How will we cope? What will the future bring?' All the lovely thoughts of baby happiness have fractured.

Eventually they take the baby home, they care for it, they nurse it, it gurgles, and it smiles like any other baby. It seems normal otherwise. It wants to be loved and hugged. It is not yet aware of its abnormality. That bridge will have to be crossed later on.

They take it out in the pram and hide the offending parts with a blanket. But eventually the awful truth of the abnormality is out. If there are other children, how will they understand or react? This family will have to be brave and helpful to one another. But often real love emerges and triumphs.

Chapter 16

When the Rains Came

Rain water, so essential, welcomed when needed, derided if it lasts too long, this elusive phenomenon, coming from the heavens, is drawn up again by the golden sun. It showers gently on our beloved blooms and earth.

The saying 'water and fire are good servants but bad masters' has been proved time and time again. The power of water can even outflank an army.

The rain in Spain stays mainly on the plain... Not so in Wales. The Merthyr to Brecon road (A470) passes the tranquil three Cwm Taf reservoirs: Llwyn On, Cantref and Beacons. Cascading little waterfalls and rivulets bubble down from the hills of the Brecon Beacons, including Pen y Fan, Cribyn and Corn Ddu.

Travellers and tourists stop by these lovely, man-made lakes to rest, to have picnics and admire the scenery. Men and boys will sit for hours just fishing.

One year in the 1980s rain excelled in Wales. And in Cardigan, County Dyfed, houses and a superstore by the Teifi were flooded and people had to be evacuated.

Where we lived, the main road leading from Llechryd to Cardigan dips downward by Llechryd Bridge then rises upwards again into the village. During heavy rain, this part, approximately 10 feet square, could fill with water and cause problems. Luckily our cottage, which was half a mile from the main road, was on an upward gradient and way above any flood. The 1980 deluge submerged the Llechryd Bridge over the Teifi completely. You couldn't see the parapet or even where the bridge was. This part, including the adjacent wide dip in the road became one large pool, big enough to swim in. It made the road to Cardigan impassable, so cars used a small by-road yards down the main road. Going round this way led them a few yards from our cottage and came out further on, past the flooded part. The large pool of water joining the river, cutting the Cardigan to Carmarthen road in half, was a truly amazing sight. People came from far and wide to view this phenomenon. Robin thought it was a new outdoor swimming pool.

The Hotel Malgwyn on the far side of the river was slightly high up, but the staff residence was right by the river edge and became flooded to the extent that the staff were trapped in upstairs rooms. A helicopter had to come and rescue them. Robin and I, with other onlookers on higher ground, watched amazed as the Malgwyn staff were hauled one by one from upstairs windows by steel winches into the safety of the helicopter and then dropped only a few yards further up by the hotel. Then the helicopter flew away. As the rain stopped slowly, bit by bit the waters subsided and the bridge and the road re-appeared, leaving sludge and flotsam for the council to clear. The road to Cardigan became passable again, the mad race of passing cars near our cottage stopped and peace reigned again.

Chapter 17

The Diabetic Child

Diabetes mellitus is caused by insulin deficiency with excess sugar in the bloodstream. The fault lies in the pancreas' (islets of Langerhans') insulin secretion. It is very serious in young people. Coma and death can result if it is untreated. Regulated diet and keeping blood sugar normal by insulin injections are the main treatment. It is a disease affecting all ages, but sadly for a young child it becomes an obstacle interfering with normal childhood. Unfortunately diabetes mellitus today is very prevalent in young children. For a young child, maybe as young as seven years old, to have to inject themselves and prick a finger to obtain a blood sample for testing sugar levels seems so cruel.

For safety's sake diabetic children carry a warning medallion around their neck and always carry an extra lump of sugar in their pocket in case of an insulin high. These children are taught to inject themselves and to recognise any early diabetic signs. It lays a heavy responsibility on a child who should be able to play without that kind of worry.

One of my granddaughters started to suffer from diabetes at the age of seven. That was 25 years ago. Then, the old-fashioned, heavy syringe, cumbersome for children, had to be separately sterilised. This has since been replaced by a small fountain-pen-like syringe, hidden in a small case which can be carried in a handbag unobtrusively. It has a press shot needle, so easy to manage, and can be administered almost anywhere quietly without attracting attention.

Going back 25 years; imagine a little girl asked to go to a party and the mother having to tell the hostess the child has diabetes and cannot have sweet goodies. Imagine the child watching others eating luscious jellies and ice cream. Imagine this child at school meals having to forgo deserts, being different from other children.

Long journeys have to be monitored. The child has to know how she feels, with the dreaded highs and lows of the diabetic illness.

My granddaughter when a child went to a diabetic holiday camp organised by the British Diabetic Association. This meant mixing with other children with the same problems, which helped them to realise they were not alone with diabetes.

My granddaughter, now grown up, has coped with diabetes all these years and lived a normal life thanks to the treatment with insulin, a lifesaver.

Chapter 18

Film Crews and the Everlasting Sermon

On a lighter note, we happened to be driving towards Cenarth Falls when we saw a camera crew and staff busy filming down by the river Teifi. This being a mid-week morning, we were the only two people there. Being curious, we stopped the car, got out and went down the embankment to have a closer look. A beautiful young girl was sitting on a rock. A woman attendant was fussing around her, combing her hair and arranging her locks to fall over her shoulder, making sure every strand was in place. A bearded man, very arty-looking – obviously either a director or producer – was directing the camera crews. He turned round and looked at Robin, Robin looked at him and held out his hand for a handshake, a friendly thing he always did when meeting people. I held my breath, waiting to be told to leave. But not so, this man of authority asked Robin for his name, shook his hand and invited us to watch the filming and even to partake of the camera crew's luscious buffet laid out in the open air on a large table.

Robin immediately felt at home; he is never one to refuse food or tea. I was just happy to watch the filming. The scene with the girl brushing her long blonde silky hair was taken again and again, at least seven times. She just patiently re-enacted it as directed.

We thanked them for their hospitality and left. They were gone the next day but we did see this commercial weeks later on the TV, several times. It was for shampoo. Robin would call out every time he saw it.

Now about the sermon that went on and on. Robin and I loved church outings. This one was organised in Llangeler, approximately 12 miles out of Cardigan. Coaches were laid on, one for Cardigan and surrounding districts and one for Carmarthen and surrounding districts. The meeting started at 7.30 p.m. Refreshments and social fellowship were to follow the sermon.

The hall was packed with the congregation and the exciting, appetising smells of the goodies to come wafted by our nostrils, much to Robin's delight. We started off with a couple of hymns that Robin liked. Then came the sermon. It was an excellent sermon, spoken in a booming kind of voice. The first half-hour was excellent. It was still good in the second half-hour. But the third seemed to be a repetition of the first one. Robin prodded me. 'When is the tea, mum?' Me: 'Hush ... hush ... soon...' The speaker's voice rose and some who had nodded off sat up with a start. Robin again: 'When is the tea?' Me again: 'Hush ... hush...' The speaker was now in the fourth half-hour. Someone came into the hall and whispered into the first person's ear in my row. The message was passed right down to me, that our coach driver was only booked to nine o'clock and would be leaving now, and unless we came now to board the coach we would have to walk home. So we all filed out past the speaker, past the lovely prepared food, me dragging an unwilling Robin back to the waiting coach and home without refreshments or socialising.

So, in the one instance, at the commercial filming, we were invited to luscious food when not expected and in the other place we had to leave before being able to partake of the promised buffet we were expecting to enjoy. I explained to Robin, 'I'm afraid we can't have everything all the time.'

Chapter 19

Leukaemia the Child Killer

Bailliere's Nurses' Complete Medical Dictionary (first published 1940) states: 'Leukaemia is a fatal blood disease in which the number of white corpuscles is largely increased.
A) Lymphatic, there is enlargement of the Lymphatic glands and spleen.
B) Myelocytic, associated with disease of the bone marrow and great enlargement of the spleen.'

It strikes all age groups, but children from very young upwards seem to be the most affected. There are many stories of these brave children battling this appalling disease. Today's treatment of up-to-date chemotherapy has been successful, but not in all cases. Imagine going through the process of debilitating chemotherapy and after feeling well for maybe a year or two then the awful cancer returns and the only thing is more treatment, more chemotherapy. For children this constant shunting from being well and full of renewed hope, then ill again and back to chemotherapy, must be heartbreaking.

There was the story of the little boy aged only seven diagnosed with leukaemia who had six remissions with the cancer returning, but the seventh was his last. He seemed so mature for his age in reasoning and accepting his ill health. He was only 12 years old when he died. His last words to his despairing mother were, 'Will you remember me when I am gone?'

The only personal experience I had with this illness in a child was when I worked as a nurse with Waltham Forest Borough Council as recorded in my memoirs *An Ordinary Woman, an Extraordinary Life*.

44

It was the case of a lost child, never to be forgotten. One of the most distressing things for a parent is to watch a beloved child who is seriously ill slipping slowly deeper into illness while you search desperately and hope for a cure.

This family hoped for a better future by emigrating. They sold all their belongings and their house and took their three children to Australia. All was fine, they started a business and did well. Then their youngest child, a girl of only seven years old, became ill. Leukaemia was diagnosed. A time of expensive treatment followed which eventually crippled their income and business. They decided that Britain with free medical treatment was the only option to save their child.

They came back to Walthamstow, where they had originally lived. They were now destitute; our housing department, who already had a waiting list an arm long, gave them a flat straight away. Yes, housing departments can be human.

The little girl attended the Great Ormond Street hospital for children. The family, now at rock bottom but with hope of a cure, started the long and debilitating treatment for their child. But to no avail. This was 40 years ago and treatment then was not as effective in children as it is today. A year after their return from Australia and extensive treatment, with the family going back and forth to Great Ormond Street hospital, the little girl died.

The Town Hall may seem a cold, unemotional place, but it is made up of people with hearts and feelings. The whole Town Hall grieved with the family. They had given up their house and friends for a better life in Australia, made new friends and success was in their grasp, then lost that too, all for the sake of a beloved child, now lost. And they had to start their lives again.

Chapter 20

Voluntary Work and the Smoker's Curse, or the Last Fag

Robin now went Monday to Friday to occupational therapy in Newcastle Emlyn. They collected him and brought him back. He took his own food with him to avoid having anything with additives, which might upset him. In winter I gave him a thermos flask with hot food and in milder weather egg salads etc. It worked well and he seemed happy.

This gave me the opportunity to do voluntary car service, which I was well acquainted with, having done this previously in the Forest of Dean.

Taking patients from around the countryside up to Bronglais hospital (Aberystwyth) and right down to Singleton hospital in Swansea helped me to get to know the whole area pretty well. I had some very odd cases to transport to and from different hospitals. At one stage there were three men all going to Bronglais hospital, one with his leg in plaster, one his arm at right angles, also in plaster, and the third with a high plaster collar round his neck. Then there was the farmer who had a hip replacement which increased his height by two inches, consequently he had to wear a shoe with heel and sole built up to equalise his walk. All this was corrected when the hospital replaced his other hip. Now two inches taller, he surpassed his two sons in height, to his delight and his sons' surprise.

Having taken patients to hospital meant having to wait until the consultants saw them and their treatment was completed before I could take them home again. This involved spending nearly all day at hospitals but I was always back in time for Robin.

There was a chain-smoking lady in Newcastle Emlyn who had

to be taken to Glangwilli hospital once a week to the chest clinic. She suffered from emphysema (of the lungs: pus in the bronchiole) due to her smoking. The journey from her home to the hospital was only half an hour. Since I did not allow smoking in my car, she used to have a fag (as she called it) in the open air outside the car before the journey and again outside at the other end of the journey in the hospital grounds. She claimed the inhaled cigarette eased her heaviness and breathing, the very thing that was actually killing her.

On the fourth journey, the last one I took her, her breathing was so bad she insisted on getting out of the car on this short journey several times. Each time I would sit patiently in the car waiting and watching her. She would be in such a state of agitation, needing an inhaling puff, her hands shaking uncontrollably in her eagerness to get the cigarette lighter to light. Eventually she would manage it. Then she had a job trying to get the lighter flame to the cigarette in her mouth. Eventually succeeding, inhaling deeply with eyes shut, she would relax with a sigh. She told me she started smoking when only 12 years old, behind the garden shed with other kids. She had tried several times to give up but each time she relapsed. She was totally and utterly addicted.

When we arrived at the hospital she told me not to wait as a friend was going to collect her and bring her home. She lit one more fag. I think it was one of the last ones she had. I was told she died on that day. She was only in her early forties.

Chapter 21

Blindness: When the Dark Curtain Descends

We accept our eyesight as our rightful norm. But sometimes this wonderful natural gift either deteriorates as age comes on or it suddenly stops. The black curtain comes down relentlessly. Those people so affected know and remember the sky is blue, grass is green and all the wondrous colours of garden blooms.

I would remember in my garden the dark blue velvety pansies smiling at me with their golden yellow star in the middle. I would remember art galleries with fantastic paintings, the fiery, powerful colours by Turner and the gentle calming water lilies by Monet. I'd remember young pretty rosy faces of smiling children. By these memories one can live in darkness and apply one's memory to everyday occurrences.

I knew such a lady in Merthyr Tydfil, Hetty Sweet, and she certainly was as sweet as her name. At less than 5 feet tall, she lived for 92 years, the last two in darkness. But she had seen and experienced the beauty of the world, its colours and shapes, before losing her sight. Her best friend and neighbour, Peggy, led her everywhere, shopping, church, church do's and outings. Hetty was always smiling and took her blindness in her stride and never complained. She lived with memories supporting her daily experiences.

But what if the dark curtain was there at the beginning of life? A blind baby, what a horrendous, slow discovery for young parents. You can care for, love and cuddle this baby. This baby will get to know you by smell, voice, touch or hugs. This baby will smile, gurgle, cry, but not be able to see you. It will be isolated when not attended to; living in a darkened world with strange sounds surrounding it. It will do all the other normal things like suckling,

48

and kicking its little legs, crying for attention and food. It will thrive. How are you going to explain and later on teach your growing blind child colours? How can you describe green as grass and blue as sky? It can touch grass and other things and feel them but not comprehend colour. You can explain the rustling of autumn leaves beneath your feet, you can explain the gentle murmuring of a bubbling stream, and you can explain the thrush's song. But colour never! Colour is something a person who is blind from birth will have to invent in their mind. They might imagine grass is blue and sky is red, if they can imagine colour at all.

There is a report of a boy born blind being cared for by his loving mum. He went to a school for the blind and was taught Braille and at home he was taught where to find everything. When he was about 11 years old, his mother became blind and he took over from her and taught her all he knew including Braille. He became her greatest help.

There are many stories of blind people rising to great heights in spite of this cruel disability. Blind Fanny Crosby wrote many beautiful hymns and was a head teacher in a school for the blind. The famous Helen Keller has had many books written about her and her governess, Miss Sullivan, who changed a frustrated rebellious blind child into a learned docile person who could speak more than one language. Helen Keller actually lost her sight through an illness at three months old. Did she recognise colours at that age? And could she remember blue sky and green grass? Or at that age was it all a blur? Do babies recognise colours and shapes at three months? Shapes yes, but colour is questionable. Then there is our own Member of Parliament David Blunkett, only one of many blind people who have reached top positions.

Chapter 22

Gambling: A Disability? Yes, Most Certainly

1) *The Arcade Child.* You see the little boy rolling his pennies into the machine, watching with want in his eyes the mass of pennies inside the glass globe slowly shifting towards the expected outlet. The excitement rises, the little heartbeat increases but the shift of pennies does not quite make it... It must make it the next time ... or the next ... or the next... Does this boy grow up to become a gambler? We don't know, but it could well be the foundation of a future gambler.

2) *Shopaholics.* They operate without back-up funds, using credit cards; this is also a form of gambling and causes distress to relationships and marriages. There was a working-class woman with more than a hundred pairs of shoes; she could not possibly wear them all. She was addicted to pretty shoes and just had to have them, and bought them whenever she saw them in a shop, or in a brochure or on the Internet. She ended up suffering from depression with financial worries.

3) *Women Gamblers?* Yes, they do exist and when they do they really go to town. The media reported a housewife whose husband gave her the mortgage money to pay into the building society and she went and gambled the lot, thinking that if she won, they could pay off the whole sum. Of course, now they are in deeper trouble.

4) *The Ordinary Gambler.* This is usually a family man. The one I knew of was fond of the 'gee gees' and dogs. He was a kind man, meant well and had a good job. His weakness, or should it be called a strong gambling addiction, had a devastating effect on his family. Who would you consider more disabled, him or them? He did not bet small amounts, oh no, the bigger the

50

stake, the bigger the winnings – or so he told his wife. 'When the ship comes in...' But the ship never came in, neither did the promised money, it was all pie in the sky. The decision they had made of the wife not going out to work till the children were of school age had to be abandoned. She took a job; the mortgage had to be paid. This family could have afforded a decent family car but had to do with an old banger. The children had second-hand clothes from jumble sales. Luxuries were out of the question; birthday parties or festivities were meagre. Holidays, oh yes they did have holidays. While other families went abroad, they stayed in hired caravans. Caravans can be great fun if you can have some treats and outings to special places, but these were off the financial menu. Ice creams? The children were lucky if they got one or two a week, while they had to watch other children enjoying them whenever the ice cream man came around. Luckily, give children a ball, a bucket and spade and they will be happy. They were promised holidays abroad, even cruises, but they never materialised. Yet the wife knew that had her husband kept his wages intact, their lives would have been totally different and they could have had a good lifestyle. This family eventually broke up due to his gambling. I knew them well. The wife could not cope any longer with a compulsive gambler and broken promises.

5) *Casino Gamblers*. They really top the lot. Thousands of pounds are gambled in casinos. Breaking the bank is rare; far more likely, thousands are lost. And it has been known for a man to gamble away house and home, goods and land and even his shirt and then go out and shoot himself.

Chapter 23

The Shame of Alcoholism

First, the man who comes home drunk and beats his wife and kids. It happens far more than we know. The man apologises when he is sober and promises not to do it again, which often is a promise meant but rarely kept. So this abuse, so debilitating to the family, sometimes goes on far too long before the family actually breaks up.

Second, I had a friend whose husband came home drunk occasionally. He would plonk himself down on the settee and start to cry like a baby. His wife would wipe his tears, help him off the settee and drag him upstairs step by step, take his shoes off and tuck him, fully dressed, into bed (to take his clothes off was too heavy for her). The next morning when he woke up, he wouldn't even remember the night before, and would wonder how he got to bed with his clothes still on.

Third, the lager louts, their fights, vandalism and destruction of property. We have all seen it on TV and read about it in the media. When off the booze, some are ordinary good citizens.

Fourth, my personal experience. She was a very special lady. Everybody liked her. She had a way with her, attracting people to her, especially teenagers, who used to visit her in her house, which was full of laughter and jokes from these young people. She made them feel important' she made everyone feel precious. But she had a secret, which she tried to hide by sucking peppermints. Everybody knew her addiction was the bottle, yet nobody had the heart to talk to her about it. We all knew she was an intelligent person, and we also knew about Alcoholics Anonymous. But by talking to her about her weakness you could lose her friendship and gain nothing for her, as I believe she had tried different avenues of

52

help, but failed each time. I was also friends with her mother, who worried herself sick. She told me that every three months or so, she would go to her daughter's bungalow and clear out empty bottles hidden in every place, inside, behind and even on top of wardrobes. Yet her daughter was such a loving person.

I too got very fond of her. She always hugged both Robin and me, and Robin really loved visiting her. She would spend time talking to him and made us feel like royalty. If there was a barbecue or party anywhere in the locality she would always invite herself and nobody ever minded because she could be so entertaining. She had married a Mexican but the marriage broke up. There were two lovely children, a boy and a girl, both with beautiful large dark eyes. I believe the family warned her she could lose the children if she didn't stop her drinking habit. She did try but wasn't strong enough to keep it up, and eventually her brother took the children into his care with the social worker's approval. Now she lived on her own.

The last time I saw her, she came to my house and sat opposite me, took my guitar and started to strum and sing to me. It was the best serenade I ever had; she had a lovely voice. That's the only time anyone serenaded me. I shall remember it for the rest of my life. She looked so beautiful with her black wavy hair and dark brown eyes; she seemed like a young girl with a rosy flush on her cheeks.

I went on holiday the next day and when I came back was told she had died that week. She was only in her thirties.

Chapter 24

Little Welsh Coffee Shops, Organic Food, Ancient Castle, Wildlife Statue and Dr David Bellamy

Cardigan was well known for quaint coffee shops, organic home produce, delicious local cakes and of course Welsh crafts. It did have a superstore but little corner shops still existed and there was plenty of choice for your table. It even had a theatre and a very good theatre company, which we sampled often.

Cardigan Castle was often in the news in 2004 because of the funding race for historic buildings. In the 1980s, when we were still there, it was in the possession of a spinster, Miss Wood, a recluse, a mere 5 feet tall, who could occasionally be seen shopping in Cardigan. She hung on tenaciously to the ownership of this now much neglected castle, I understood, in spite of the council's bid to take over and renovate it. The castle and ground were high up over the Cardigan to Carmarthen main road and a high wall was supposed to keep part of it from sliding onto the traffic. But this wall leaned dangerously towards the road and collapse seemed imminent. The worried council reinforced it with strong iron girders.

I was intrigued what mysteries lay behind these high, forbidding walls and Robin and I went to find out. We were lucky on the day we called as Miss Wood was in and happened to be near the big rusty iron gate. I asked her whether we could see inside. She ignored me but looked at Robin and asked him why he wanted to come in. To my embarrassment he gave one of those double-dutch answers and to my surprise Miss Wood said curtly, 'Come on in then, but you'll have to pay.' I think Robin's obvious disability made her feel kindly towards him. Being a recluse, she probably felt a little kinship as regards social isolation. She charged us £6.

We were the only people visiting that day. I felt honoured to be allowed in, due to Robin, where others had failed. She pushed the old large creaky gate open and we entered rather timidly.

She did not show us around but left us to our own devices. We felt a little like Alice in a neglected Wonderland. There were weeds and brambles everywhere, paths unrecognisably overgrown like a jungle, dark passages going underground, where we would venture a few steps then give up, afraid of their unsafe state. There were a lot of strange rustling noises and movements in the undergrowth. Were they cats, rabbits, birds or mice or even snakes? We trod softly and carefully. We didn't dare to visit the ivy-overgrown old house where we knew she had retired. We roamed for about an hour in this adventurous place then went home, extracting thorns and other beasties from our clothes and hair.

One day we were having a quiet day at home sitting in front of our cottage admiring the garden when there was a sudden terrific roar above us and all the shrubs and flowers in our garden bowed and swayed in a heavy current of wind. A helicopter was zooming above us and appeared to be coming down behind our cottage. We rushed round to see it landing in the field behind us. The well-known botanist Dr David Bellamy alighted. He had come to stay at the big house at the end of our lane, as next day he would be unveiling a bronze statue of an otter sculpted by Geoffrey Powell which was presented to Cardigan on behalf of Dyfed Wildlife Trust's golden jubilee. Dr Bellamy did the honour of unveiling this beautiful statue at a ceremony on a Thursday in August 1988.

A part of the excitement of that day was that we had the pleasure of seeing Dr Bellamy and the helicopter so close to our own ancient cottage.

Chapter 25

Brittle Bone Disease

Brittle bone disease (*Osteogenesis imperfecta*), is characterised by abnormal fragility of the bones with liability to fracture.

The little girl, she couldn't have been more than seven years old, suffered from brittle bone disease but her life was made bearable by a Labrador dog, as documented on TV.

She was in a wheelchair, isolated from other children. She could only watch from her window as they played, ran around and rode their bikes. She lived in a world of her own, lonely, yearning to be like others, be with others, to be out there and join in. Inside her home she would watch the family busy doing daily tasks. She had to wait patiently for everything to be done for her, washing, dressing, even cutting up food. Being pushed in the wheelchair for walks in the park was always a special treat when time allowed. But if only she could do this herself, if only... Kind friends and neighbours did visit her and bring her presents to brighten her life.

Then came the best gift ever, a Labrador dog. There are some people who keep special dogs to take for hospital visits to children's wards as children bond lovingly with animals, and animals help with the healing therapy. So this little girl received a Labrador dog, a kind of guide dog to whom she took to straight away, and her life changed dramatically. At first she just loved him to bits for his gentleness, loyalty and comradeship. Then she was taught that this lovely pet could give her the independence and freedom which had eluded her so far. This dog could bring on demand most of her wants. And, most of all, what joy, she could now be wheeled out in her wheelchair with him beside her, pulling her and being a sort of protector and guide. This too took a burden off the rest of the family and she could venture out frequently to the park, where the other children immediately befriended her and admired and petted her guide dog.

There is only one sad thing about loving and owning a guide dog or indeed any other pet. Their lifespan is much shorter than ours. The deep grief when losing a beloved pet cannot be described. And in the case where a person needs such a pet, like a blind person, this loss will occur more than once in their lifetime. A daunting task.

Fathers of Disabled Children

About fathers of disabled children: there are three types.

1) The father who stands by his wife and the disabled child she bore him. He is a good man and knows where his responsibility is. He loves and cares for his family regardless of circumstance.

2) Alas, the man who abandons the woman with the disabled child she bore him. He is the type who likes to have freedom and fun, and feels any responsibility a tie and a burden, interfering with his lifestyle. He does not want to know, he does not care about the hurt to the woman who bore his child nor the innocent child who might feel unloved by her father and might even feel guilty of being the cause of his leaving, because of her disability. He is a cad.

3) There is a kind of man who falls in love with a woman with a disabled child who is not even his own. For the love of her he takes on and loves her child, he shares the problems of family life, he is a real man with the instinct to protect and care for a vulnerable woman and her child. There can be no deeper love and that family unit is surely blessed.

Yes, I knew and came into contact during my nursing career with all three types: the ordinary one, the abandoning one, and the adopting hero.

Chapter 26

The Strange Energy and Life Force of Small Creatures, and When Death Gives the Gift of Life

Cardigan had many wonders to offer if you were of an inquiring mind. I tried to give Robin an all-round life experience while enjoying it myself at the same time. There was a wildlife area near the river Teifi, with mostly birds, otters and other creepy crawlies. Approximately 3 miles out of Cardigan town was a butterfly sanctuary with some rare and beautiful butterflies, which we visited more than once. Robin called them 'flutter bys'. I was fascinated by their ability to fly in such a hot and humid place as this almost air-still sanctuary, as I had explained to Robin that flight was only possible in currents of air. I read somewhere that a jet aeroplane flies by their turbo jet engines' creation of strong air turbulence, which lifts and flies the plane. But this didn't explain how butterflies could fly in a still and hot atmosphere with their delicate fragile wings, wings that we dared not touch for fear of causing damage. I can understand an eagle's enormous wing span, and its wings flapping supporting this beautiful wild bird. But this does not explain how a bumblebee's heavy body, supported by only small, thin, almost transparent wings, can buzz around. We were still mystified. Robin would listen attentively, but I don't know if he took any of it in. The most intriguing thing to me was this strong life force which produced their flights. Such small bodies weighing practically nothing, had so much energy, and so much vigour. Their wing colours too were fantastic, especially the red admiral, the tortoiseshell and the peacock.

Then there was the Cardigan aquarium, another place we frequented. Again the colour patterns on some of the tropical fish were fantastic, out of this world. Some of the smaller species, no bigger than a matchstick, darted here, there and everywhere. These small living creatures with eyes, hearts and all the other biological necessities in their minute bodies were a wonder of wonders.

Larger life could be observed behind our cottage where sheep would graze, and they too were interesting, the way the little lambs seemed to grow so fast and nearly match their ewe mothers' height. In early 1980 when we had a very late, nearly end of spring snowfall during the lambing season, the little lambs were buried in the snow and the retired Commodore in residence at that time in the big house at the end of the lane helped the farmer to dig out ewes and lambs. It was all hands aboard and everybody came out to help and so got to know each other.

Robin had a habit of wandering off sometimes, but he always came back. The farmer's young son in his late teens brought him back once or twice. He was a very charming young man and assured me it was no problem and he enjoyed being of use. This same young man carried a donor card because his father had a diseased kidney. I wondered if this was due to the poisonous sheep dipping. Did they wear protective clothing and masks all those years ago? Or was it some other causing factor? This young man went away on holiday, possibly to Cyprus, with his motor bike. Tragically he had a fatal accident. His kidney was flown back to Wales for his father.

Can anyone comprehend the trauma of this family? A precious young son lost. A new life gained by the father.

Chapter 27

The Curse of Epilepsy

Bailliere's Nurses' Complete Medical Dictionary defines epilepsy as: a nervous disease characterised by fits of unconsciousness with convulsions, often proceeded by strange sensations e.g. 'aura'.

1. *petit mal* (French for little harm). Symptoms: only momentary loss of consciousness, but no convulsions.

2. *grand mal* (French for big harm). Symptoms: loss of consciousness, which may be accompanied by the 'epileptic cry'. The tongue may be bitten and urine passed unconsciously. The fit is followed by deep sleep.

The first, petit mal can be quite frightening when it first happens, but is nothing in comparison with grand mal. Imagine your beloved child suddenly going into a fit of unconsciousness with contractions, tremors and this dreadful 'epileptic cry'. Panic and fear of death grip the parents. When the first attack is over and after several visits to the doctor and hospital and the diagnosis is confirmed, then comes the awful realisation that this was not a 'one off', but may occur again and again. Our poor child, how are we going to cope? Do we know when such an attack may occur next' Can we organise outings away from public places and crowds in case of . . . ? What about school and holidays? While the parents' main object is to protect their child, at the same time they try to hide this terrible disease from friends and neighbours.

Although there are stabilising medications available, they do not completely eradicate all the symptoms, but they certainly minimise them. The lady I knew who had epilepsy, when on the medication she would get the preliminary 'aura' sensation and would cry out 'mum ... mum...', but never lost consciousness nor experienced unpleasant tremors.

I worked for six months in a mental hospital in 1961, over 40 years ago. To my shock and horror I found a great many people who should never have been incarcerated there. They were epilepsy sufferers, a disease shunned then. They had been abandoned by their families, who were ashamed of them and sent them out of sight, out of mind ... and out of responsibility. In this mental hospital I came across a woman who was in a side ward. She was lame and on top of that disability also suffered from epilepsy. Today she could have been cared for at home. Being in a mental hospital made her bitter and uncooperative. She had the label 'beware, she bites'. The side ward she was in had a round observation window and I observed her one night as she went into a fit, trembling and shaking. I went in, in spite of having been told not to worry as she could not harm herself and she could hurt me. Anyway, I could not see her alone in this state and went in and held her hand firmly and stayed until the attack was over. This patient let me change, nurse or do anything for her and never showed any aggression towards me. Did she remember, or had she recognised the time I was there to comfort her? This poor, now middle-aged lady had a women's magazine cover picture of a young good-looking woman lovingly holding a baby. This faded picture she kept under her pillow and she would not let anyone take it away from her.

Chapter 28

Aids, the Fatal Pandemic Curse

My *Bailliere's Nurses' Dictionary* (last edition 1941), does not describe Aids, it just did not exist then. Aids is the acronym for acquired immune deficiency syndrome and stands for HIV, human immune deficiency, the virus causing Aids. This means the immunity defence system of the body has ceased to function and the body is unprotected against any infection.

Aids reared its tragic ugly head in the UK in 1981 when the first patient with this disease lay dying in a London hospital. The USA had already had 200–300 cases.

In 1984 French scientists uncovered the causing agent. A vaccine has yet to be found, although laboratories are trying frantically to find one. Aids, once diagnosed, often means a death sentence. At the beginning, with it being an infectious disease, people treated those suffering from Aids like lepers.

At first this disease was thought to be in young male homosexuals only, but it slowly escalated to heterosexuals, then women, mothers and babies (uterine infection from the mother). Many of the women were innocent victims, their husband or partner having strayed sexually and infected not only them but the unborn child as well.

The number of people with Aids diagnosed in the USA in 1995 rose to over 415,000 cases. More than half had already died of this disease. Now the estimated number of infected persons in the USA is over one million. Aids spread into other continents, Europe, Asia, Africa and Australia, etc. In Asia and Africa it has been enormous. Globally the number of infected persons (including children and babies) could be 20–40 million diagnosed cases, according to *HIV and Aids* by Robert Pratt (Hodder Arnold, 2003).

At risk are drug addicts sharing needles and those having casual unprotected sex.

Aids sufferers are apt to get tuberculosis and pneumonia, amongst other infections, which hastens their death. We see much about this illness on TV and in the media. We see poor little African babies in makeshift hospitals afflicted with Aids passed on to them by their infected mothers. They have no hope of survival: we know they are dying. I think of our late Princess Diana, hugging little ones in Africa on her visits and comforting their mothers.

In the younger generation, the one-night stand, where you don't know or even care who it is you are having sex with and ask no questions, can lead to Aids, since this disease is mostly transmitted by sexual intercourse. You don't know whether your partner is free from Aids and who else he has been with. He or she may be HIV positive even if the symptoms have not yet arisen, and you are caught. There is nothing as sad as a young life terminated by perhaps one sexual adventure, maybe while under the influence of alcohol.

I knew such a young man and his family. He had a brilliant future, and loving parents and friends. He became seriously ill and to everybody's shock, died of Aids. He was only 29 years old. Apart from the trauma and grief, there was the shame, in those days, of everybody knowing the young man died of Aids. That was the time the family, in their grief, found out who were their true friends.

Chapter 29

Tuberculosis, the Sinister Creeper

Tuberculosis is a specific infectious disease caused by the bacillus tuberculosis discovered by Koch. Symptoms: emaciation, loss of appetite, loss of weight, loss of strength, night sweats and rising fever.

There is tuberculosis of the lungs – phthisis; the skin – lupus; the blood – miliary; and it also occurs in other parts of the body, like the spine.

Bovine tuberculosis is transferred by infected milk from cows, and attacks the glands mainly in the neck. Sterilisation of milk was introduced to protect children from bovine tuberculosis.

When I worked for Waltham Forest Borough Council as infection control nurse, I was in charge of entering infectious disease notifications. Books of these entries had been kept, going right back to the 1920s. Notifications came in at that time at the rate of approximately 20 each week. Imagine this multiplied by all the other London boroughs and then the rest of the whole country. This was in epidemic proportions. Apart from sterilising milk and the Mantoux test (a test for existent tuberculosis in humans by injection of tuberculin into the skin, which was introduced by French physician Mantoux 1877–1956). By this test, early treatable tuberculosis infection could be diagnosed by the reaction on the skin site. Thirteen-year-old children were tested in this way. If infected they were treated, if free from this infection they were vaccinated.

In the 1920s it must have also emerged in other countries that tried all kinds of preventative measures. I remember as a child in

64

Switzerland notices erected in streets '*Spucken Verboten*' (spitting banned) to stop people spitting phlegm onto the road where people might pick up infection on their shoes and bring it into their homes.

In Hollywood, filmmakers soon realised the tragedies this disease caused. There were then many films and plays on this theme. The film which I remember most was *Camille*, where Robert Taylor and Greta Garbo have a passionate love affair and Greta Garbo dies in Robert Taylor's arms of tuberculosis.

My own personal involvement with this disease was during my training at King's College hospital in London. Firstly I was asked to clear a maid's room of her belongings so that they could be packed and collected by her parents. She had been diagnosed as suffering from tuberculosis and was sent to a hospital near her home. Amongst all her things were empty bottles and bottles of cough mixture, asthma inhalers and bronchial lozenge sweet tins. This poor girl tried to cure her persistent cough by herself and in so doing became terminally ill.

The second case was of a young man suffering from tuberculosis. Due to the war and shortage of space (upstairs wards were closed due to bomb scares), some tuberculosis patients were put at the end of wards near balconies where we were able to push them outside into the fresh air, weather permitting. Although they were at the end of the ward they had screens around them separating them from the main ward. These patients were strictly 'barrier nursed', which meant fresh gowns, masks and rubber gloves each time you entered the screens and you discarded them in disinfecting pails when leaving. All crockery and utensils were sterilised. This young man called out in distress and I went to his aid with mask, gown etc. He was sitting upright gasping for air; I called for assistance and put my arm around his shoulder to support him. He literally died in my arms just as the sister arrived. It seemed to me he drowned in his own fluid-ridden lung. He was only 19 years old.

The third case was of a different type, in a private wing, a beautiful young blonde girl. She was so very delicate and charming; she had been diagnosed to be suffering from tuberculosis because she had a persistent cough. She was near the end of her treatment and waiting to go to Switzerland's pure alpine air for recuperation. She was engaged to be married to the famous pianist Louis Kentner; not only that but her sister married the famous violinist Yehudi

Menuhin. To thank the hospital staff for caring for and nursing his future bride, Louis Kentner had a grand piano installed on the King's College hospital ground floor and played one of Chopin's famous waltzes. All the doors to the ward, clinics, casualty etc. were opened and the strands of this lovely music vibrated and echoed throughout the hospital.

Chapter 30

Lotty the Ferocious Nanny Goat

My eldest daughter Jennifer, who bought a cottage near me when we lived in the Forest of Dean, had a nanny goat. This goat supplied her family with milk. Being told by farmers of the goodness of goat's milk I thought it might benefit Robin. The local newspaper carried an advertisement 'Nanny goat for sale, good milker', so my daughter thought of having a second goat so that I could have the milk, providing I did the milking. I was all for it. Milking was no problem as I had milked goats when up in the Alps in Switzerland.

So we decided to go and have a look at this nanny goat. We piled into my 'Beetle', Jennifer and her two children, Clive, five years old and Lucy, seven years old, Robin and myself, and we drove down to Monmouth. We had a job to find the place but eventually got there. The woman owner seemed very eager and asked us to sit on a bench outside her house while she fetched Lotty. 'Lotty who?' I asked. 'Oh Lotty is the nanny goat,' she said, and trundled off to get Lotty, disappearing behind her house. We sat and waited.

There seemed to be a kind of commotion going on behind the house. There were noises of coaxing, then the woman appearing, frantically pulling a rope, but barely in view and being pulled back out of sight again. This comedy of being pulled forwards and backwards into our view and out again lasted for about 15 minutes, the woman calling out time and again, 'Come on, Lotty!' Eventually she must have grabbed Lotty by the collar, which gave her more control, and dragged Lotty into full view. We all stood up eager to see this disturbance-causing creature.

Lotty was much bigger than we expected and had enormous horns and a menacing look in her eyes. On seeing us she started

67

to kick and scrape her back legs like a bull about to charge. Clods of earth were flying up – only smoke coming from her nostrils was missing. Little Clive hid behind me, peering around anxiously, sucking his thumb. But the woman held onto Lotty for dear life. I said shakily, 'Are you sure this is a nanny goat and not a buck?' She said in a hurt sort of offended way, 'Can't you see her dear little udders?' and to the nanny goat, 'Steady girl, these nice people are going to look after you'. Not on your nelly, I thought, giving Jennifer an eye-rolling look.

Jennifer wanted to know where the goat had been kept at night. The woman seemed reluctant to oblige this information, but Jennifer insisted. The woman then tied Lotty to an iron ring on her house and led us round the back. We just stared in disbelief: there was a wooden shed with nearly all its timber wall planks in shreds, kicked out or fallen down. The door hung precariously on one hinge. The roof was partly sliding down one side, nearly touching the ground. The place looked a mess; a wreck would describe it more accurately.

Obviously Lotty, with her big horns, had had a field day and equally obviously the sale was off.

Chapter 31

Alzheimer's Disease

Chambers Dictionary: 'Alzheimer's disease ... an illness affecting the brain and causing dementia in the middle-aged or elderly.' [Alois Alzheimer (1864–1915), German neurologist.]

Tucked in a corner of a national newspaper in 2004 appeared a short article: the journalist and broadcaster Bernard Levin had died at 70 years of age after battling with Alzheimer's disease. During the sixties, he was on the satirical *That Was the Week that Was* TV show. The famous and controversial journalist wrote for *The Times* between 1971 and 1997. The short paragraph hid a slow, long, insidious illness, which can take years to reach its eventual termination (death). It can have a devastating effect on the rest of the family while the patient is unaware of what is happening to him.

Bernard Levin was only one of many famous people affected by this destructive illness, as it does not differentiate between rich, poor or famous.

A friend's husband started with this Alzheimer's early as he was only 50 years old. During his young life he had worked up a successful business, which eventually collapsed due to his illness. The wife had to give up her job to care for him full-time. Once a year, social services would take him away for a fortnight into a home to give the family a break and an opportunity for an un-harassed holiday. To watch a beloved husband slipping slowly into dementia is tragic, especially as there is no cure as yet. Maybe years ahead, but too late for today's sufferers.

Then there was a couple who had been married 50 years, looking forward to their golden wedding celebration with their whole family, but by then the husband was in a home as the aged wife could not cope or care for him at home any longer. He suffered with Alzheimer's disease. She visited him daily even when she was in her eighties; she loved him still in spite of the fact that he didn't even recognise her. Her visits would consist of bringing toiletries, fresh pyjamas, flowers and little goodies. She would just sit quietly, sometimes talking softly to him and then leaving, repeating the same things each day. Did he know she was there? Or was he completely vague, the way he appeared? She didn't know. All she wanted to do was to be with him, sitting there quietly.

She could still see little fragments of his old self appear now and then. And just as these fragments appeared, so they would disappear again.

Women too are affected. There was the husband who cared for his sick wife with Alzheimer's disease at home and even took her out, pushing her in a wheelchair to get her into the fresh air, and he himself a pensioner. He tried to keep her out of a home for as long as possible; he felt he owed that much for the loving, loyal years they had had together, but eventually he had to let her go to the professional people in a home who could better care for her. These relatives, husbands, wives, friends and offspring live on the memories of their loved ones now past normality and how they were before this disease gripped them.

One private home I visited had a wife and husband as residents. Before admission to this home he apparently used to wander off not knowing where he was and this became a dangerous practice. He would stand for hours in one spot till some kind person realised something was wrong and called the police or an ambulance, while his wife would worry herself sick till he was found. This was when he was admitted to the home. I don't know why the wife was in the home with him, as she seemed all right. She probably had a physical disability of some sort and could not cope living on her own and running a home. He could converse with you sometimes and was probably at the beginning of his illness.

Chapter 32

Friends and Honeybees and Day Outings

As I have mentioned, I had three beehives in my little orchard at the bottom of my garden in the Forest of Dean. To help me to care for them I got in touch with the local bee-keeping association, who in turn introduced me to a local bee-keeper, Mr Edmunds. He and his wife were in their eighties and they were the loveliest people I had ever met. When meeting Robin they took to him straight away and Robin always seemed relaxed and happy in their company. The reason was that both these gentle people talked to him as if he was the most important person in the world and his confused talk did not matter. Mr Edmunds was an experienced bee-keeper and he helped me to check the beehives on a regular basis. Robin would enjoy watching both of us dressed up with hats, veils and all the other paraphernalia to protect against bee stings.

Apart from helping us with the bees, he took my grandson Michael fishing while he was staying with me. Robin and I were often invited to Mr and Mrs Edmunds' house in Bream for tea (she made lovely scones and sometimes apple pies) and they took us many times to Abergavenny for fish and chips. One summer we were invited to their caravan in Porthcawl by the sea for the day and had a wonderful time. They were like loving parents to us.

At the end of the season Mr Edmunds came (dressed up in special hat, veil etc.) to help me take out the honeycombs. He would show me how to smoke the bees into docility so we could take the honey frames out without being stung. He told me that the smoke would make the bees think there was a forest fire and they then filled themselves with honey to take with them to safety. He also showed me the queen bee and helped me put a yellow dot on her so I could always recognise her and know where she was and what she was up to. This was all very interesting to me though I don't know whether Robin took it all in. I was allowed to use Mr Edmunds' honey extractor and we always filled many jars with lovely pale yellow honey. The honey must have come from the many lime trees in the Forest of Dean that the bees used to visit.

We couldn't possibly eat all the honey ourselves so, apart from giving a lot to friends and relations, I sold quite a few pounds.

The sad thing was Mr Edmunds, now in his late eighties, fell down the stairs in his home, lost a lot of blood from his injuries and died soon afterwards. And as it usually is with two people who lived with and loved each other for so many years, Mrs Edmunds followed him to the grave soon afterwards. We were moving at that time and I never told Robin what had happened to the Edmunds, as he would have been too upset.

The times that we spent with this lovely old couple were some of the happiest during my retirement. I think back with only fond memories of those days especially as Robin was very happy as well.

Chapter 33

Meningitis, Parents' Worst Nightmare

Meningoccal meningitis: inflammation of the meninges (the membrane covering the brain and spinal cord).

Early symptoms are severe headache, fever, photo phobia (sometimes with a squint), followed in more severe cases by delirium, rigidity of neck muscles, obisthotonus (spine arching backwards due to spasms in the region).

When a child has a mild fever the first worry is: should we call a busy doctor? Or is it just a childish upset? With children, if there is a fever the wisest thing is to call out the doctor, as little children can deteriorate very quickly. The doctor does not mind. He would rather be called out early than too late. In a case of meningitis, early diagnosis is a must. Today's antibiotics are dramatic lifesavers, whereas before these wonderful drugs existed, meningitis was fatal.

Although meningitis is associated with children it can affect any age group. Young people and especially students (who tend to burn the candle at both ends, partying, late nights, lack of sleep, over-exerting their bodies etc.) are vulnerable.

Elderly folk too can be affected. I myself in my late seventies was rushed off to hospital with meningitis after calling the doctor. Due to his prompt diagnosis I was on treatment with antibiotic drugs almost straight away and was home from the hospital in less than a fortnight.

The saddest case I was involved in was when I was an infection control nurse for Waltham Forest Borough Council. A young mother of three young children died of meningitis within 24 hours of calling the doctor. It is possible that she had mild symptoms for a day or two but ignored them as she was too busy caring for her family until it was too late, giving herself a death sentence and leaving behind a bewildered, devastated husband with three motherless children. Needless to say, everybody involved with this family at this tragic time was suffering with them.

I had the task of taking throat swabs from the rest of the family and the only one carrying this deadly bug was the school child. She was a symptom-less carrier and had to be treated to clear her prior to going back to school. The class she was in was also investigated for carriers but they were found free from infection.

The fact that the child did not develop the disease proves that it is possible for people to carry but not be affected by this terrifying bug, depending how healthy they are.

Chapter 34

Robin to the Rescue

On a lovely Saturday afternoon we decided to drive into the unknown Dyfed countryside to explore. We drove along places we hadn't been to before, outside Newcastle Emlyn. There was a small road with bushes either side that we had passed many times and wondered where it led. We had seen riders trotting along the little lane, so down it we went. It wound round and round till it came to open fields, when the road became a muddy track and, oh dear, the car got stuck in the mud. No matter how hard I tried to accelerate, the wheels just rotated round and round, with mud being splattered all over the place.

I realised we needed help. Phone the AA? I hadn't a mobile. So what? We seemed miles from anywhere. In the distance we could see the outline of a building at least half a mile ahead. Was it an empty place or a farm? I decided one of us had to go and find out. But who? Because I had seen riders on this little road, the possibility was there might be some coming by who might be able to help, so one of us had to stay by the car. I decided that Robin, being the more mobile on foot, should go to this house with a note from me in case his confusion got the better of him when he got there. The note said: 'Help, we're stuck with our car in the mud'. I let him go with an anxious prayer in my heart and trustfully watched him trotting off towards our hope of help. As his image got smaller and smaller in the distance, my worry got worse and worse. What was I thinking of, letting a disabled young man go alone to an unknown place? I cannot remember how long I waited in desperate misery before I saw a large contrivance slowly moving towards where we were stuck. On top I could distinguish two people and I knew one was Robin. Was this a harvester or other farm machinery? Never mind, my heart leapt for joy. Robin had done his errand well. When they arrived Robin still had his folded note in his hand the way I had given it to him. He must have told the farmer himself about our mishap without confusion. The farmer looked at me bemused. 'There's a kettle of fish, bach,' he said and tied a rope from our car to his tractor and had us out in no time and facing the right way home.

I did offer compensation but he wouldn't hear of it. 'Glad to be of help,' he said and got on his tractor and went back to his farm. So Robin had come up trumps when it was needed and I was proud of him. My hero! But I never ventured into unknown territory again.

We went swimming one day during the summer holidays. There were plenty of children in the pool. I was waiting at the shallow end (4 feet deep) for Robin to be shot out of the water chute tunnel. Two little girls approximately 10 years old were competing near me to see who could stay under water the longest. They took it in turns to dive under, holding their breath and pinching their noses, and the one who was out of the water counted. As Robin splashed out from the water chute and joined me he saw the diving girl nearly at the bottom of the pool and without hesitation went under and pulled her up by her arm. He thought she was in difficulty. She wasn't pleased, but I was. It proved Robin's heart was in the right place.

Chapter 35

Asthma, the Social Hidden Curse

Bailliere's Nurses' Dictionary: 'Asthma is a paroxysmal affection of the bronchial tubes giving rise to dyspnoea (laboured breathing), cough and sense of suffocation. True asthma is an expiratory dyspnoea, may be due to nervous irritation of the bronchial mucous membrane, paroxysmal or chronic and often runs in families.'

Chambers Dictionary: 'A chronic disorder of the organs of respiration [lungs] characterized by difficulty of breathing, wheezing, and a tightening in the chest.'

Asthma is most distressing when it affects young children. Imagine the fear and panic in both child and parent during the first attack when, in its mother's arms, the child fights for its breath and there is the fear of death. I experienced this distressing condition at first hand as Robin suffered with wheezy attacks while under five years old. There were many nights I held him in my arms, willing him to breathe, suffering with him. Somehow these attacks always seemed to come at night. As mentioned before, we took him for swimming lessons hoping to strengthen his lungs. These attacks then diminished and stopped when he was about 10 years old. I don't know if this was due to swimming or if they would have stopped anyway, as many young children seem to grow out of this disabling condition.

Not so with adults, whose asthma seems to be of a chronic nature. The man or woman with an inhaler ever at hand is a common occurrence in today's questionable environment of smoking, industrial output and car exhaust fumes. Even dust mites and other allergies seem to be blamed.

But imagine being prone to this condition, never knowing when the next attack will occur. It can come any time: while on public transport, with friends, at a party or at the cinema or theatre, gives you no advance warning. Consider the embarrassment of the distressed panic breathing, having to disappear with an inhaler to somewhere hidden and trying to regain normal breathing. This must be a nightmare. Carrying an inhaler brings comfort but at the same time is a constant reminder of this hidden, distressful condition

The sad part is that apparently asthma in children is on the increase and more prevalent than in the adult population, and even children carry inhalers to treat themselves. Living in towns and near factories puts the population more at risk. But if you happen to be employed by these factories you have no choice but to live near them, unless you want to commute miles every day from the country to protect your children.

Chapter 36

The Mushroom Rage Man

Robin loved mushrooms. So when the season was right, off we went to the nearest field which was well endowed with this naturally grown food. We three, Robin, Melissa, now seven years old, and I (Michael had by now gone back to his father after passing his 11 plus) started out very early, about 7 a.m. and soon had our baskets full of mushrooms.

We were just about to walk home when a big and equally wide man came bellowing after us. I gathered he was complaining that we had trespassed on his field and taken his mushrooms. I didn't like the look on his face nor the angry way he came towards us, so I emptied all three baskets in a pile by his gate, called out 'sorry' and rushed off, dragging Melissa along, followed by Robin. I didn't wait for him to reach us as his demeanour seemed full of rage, I called it 'mushroom rage', and my concern was for my little granddaughter and Robin.

When I went to collect my usual dozen farm eggs, I told the farmer all about our mushroom adventure. He said that the field next to the one where we were told off belonged to him and we were welcome to gather mushrooms there. Delighted, we set off the very next morning walking past the cottage where we had left our mushroom collection. To our surprise the pile of mushrooms we had left the day before was still there; he hadn't even bothered to pick them up. So much for his rage at losing his mushrooms. As a further surprise, to our slight embarrassment, he sat outside his cottage, large as life, with arms folded across his chest and elbows resting on his beer belly, legs outstretched before him and a piercing eagle *'you dare'* look under his bushy eyebrows. He was obviously sitting there to protect his field against us three 'vagrants'.

We ignored him and went to the next field, which did not belong to him, and gathered until our baskets were full, then walked by his cottage on our way back home. He was still sitting there glaring at us. I walked by nonchalantly and to reassure little anxious Melissa I hummed 'All Things Bright and Beautiful', with Robin trailing behind not being aware of anything amiss. When home in our cottage we had mushrooms on toast for breakfast and discussed 'the mushroom rage man' and wondered why he had not retrieved his mushrooms, which we had gathered for him for free the day before.

Chapter 37

Deafness and Muteness

(A Major or Minor Disability?)

It could be both. Hearing loss when in a crowd or company isolates you completely. You are locked in a silent world. Luckily today's hearing aids can help the hard of hearing out of this problem. Age-related deafness seems the most prevalent.

Otoscerosis (a formation of spongy bone in the capsule of the labyrinth of the ear) is another form of deafness.

Then there is deafness in newborn babies, which can now be detected by a special test within hours of birth. It is estimated that over 800 deaf babies are born every year. Before this test, parents would take their babies home unaware of this disability. Only in time would they realise something was wrong. Their baby would not react to noise, talking or music and eventually they would seek professional help and advice and learn their baby was deaf and something could be done about it.

Deafness or partial deafness in school children is often missed and only diagnosed after the child's failure to progress.

There is also Menière's disease syndrome (named after the French physician Menière 1799–1862), a disorder characterised by attacks of dizziness, buzzing noises in the ear and progressive deafness due to chronic disease of the labyrinth of the ear.

The deaf and mute (both deaf and dumb) problem so courageously borne by those who are afflicted is amazing. Sign language is a complete springboard to communication amongst their peers. I have learned one or two of their signs and find it fascinating watching two deaf and mute people talking to each other in this language. I believe the deaf and mute have their own social clubs and meetings.

In my own experience of being deaf before receiving my hearing aid, I felt like a fool when in company, saying yes whenever spoken to so as not to offend. Of course once I said yes when I shouldn't have and got myself into trouble, which I found out later on, to my shock and horror. But the people concerned knew of my hard of hearing problem, and what could have been a disaster became a joke.

Chapter 38

Depression

Chambers Dictionary: 'A stage of deep dejection and a pervasive feeling of helplessness, together with apathy and loss of self-esteem, causing retardation of thought and bodily functions.'

Depression is not mentioned in my *Bailliere's Nurses' Dictionary*. It either did not exist in 1940 or was not recognised as an illness or disability.

When the lights go down and there's nothing left to be.
When the lights go down and truth is all you see.
And I wonder if all life's about the sum of all my doubts,
When the lights go down.

For me, this song recorded by Faith Hill, a well-known country music artist, describes depression, its depths, heart search and questions.

What brings depression on? We don't always know. There are several kick-off factors. Post-natal depression after a traumatic birth leaves the mother often unable to bond with her baby, giving her a guilt complex and driving her into depression. There are some medications that will help. Luckily this depression is usually of short duration.

Bereavement, stress and misfortune can last much longer and when treated with drugs, while very helpful, can often leave the patient addicted. A friend of mine lost three members of her family in one year, one being her beloved son of 19 years in a car crash. She sat in her room day and night with her head in her hands. She could not go out and face people. She had counselling and medication and slowly regained her equilibrium, but it took nearly a year. But this wasn't the end of the story; she was left with a prescribed medication addiction which took her another year to conquer.

Then you get the teenager overburdened before important exams, with parents hoping for only the best from their offspring plus pressure from peers and teachers. The resulting depression can be so serious it can be almost suicidal.

Depressive patients are rarely admitted into hospital and when they are they are usually admitted into psychiatric wards.

There have been many stories on TV and in the media about the sad side effects of addiction to the drugs used to treat depression and the lengths taken to get rid of this scourge.

It seems that depression is on the increase and is a malady of the well-to-do countries; it is hardly seen in poor countries where people are starving and having to fight for their living. And even if it was, there would not be the medication available as we are used to for free.

Chapter 39

The Bully

(A disability? Most Certainly to the Victim)

We have all heard of the school bully in the media. Apart from the distress caused by bullying, the bully can intimidate his victim to silence: 'Don't you dare snitch...' It takes a long time before parents and teachers become aware of what is happening to a timid child and the psychological effects can be devastating. I have already described in Chapter 2 how Robin was bullied mercilessly at his comprehensive school in Chingford.

Of course bullying can take place in other places, in institutions, at work and even at home, from a brother or even father, which is even worse because the child has no one to turn to.

And would you believe, it can even happen in hospital, where you feel you should be protected as a patient. Hospital bullies could be nurses, sisters, patients or in some hospitals even the matron (most certainly not at King's College Hospital, London – where I did my training, 1942–46. The matron, Miss K. Blyde OBE, was charming and more like a mother to her staff).

I worked on a medical ward which had three old dears at one end. There was nothing wrong physically, they were just old and bedridden and needed nursing care. They appeared to have no families, or if they did, they did not want to know.

One old lady was very timid and shy, but the one in the next bed was devious and sometimes even nasty. She used to smoke, which was forbidden. When the nurses were busy elsewhere she would puff away under her sheet, a wonder she did not set herself alight. If the matron came along sniffing, she'd play the innocent and point at her neighbour's bed. The timid one would just hide beneath her sheet. The matron knew who the real culprit was and would walk on shaking her head. I believe this naughty old girl even once swallowed a cigarette end to hide her guilt. She was also a bully at her ripe old age of 90 years. She took a delight in worrying her timid neighbour by pointing a crooked finger at her and chanting in her loud croaking voice:

Bubble, bubble, toil and trouble, earth to earth, and dust to dust,
    If God won't have you the devil sure must...

The timid one would shiver and hide under her sheet and we had eventually to move her away from her tormentor and put the bully next to the wall, with another fighting-fit old dear as her neighbour.

Chapter 40

Arthritis and Osteoarthritis

Arthritis ... inflammation of a joint associated with swelling, pain stiffness, etc.

Osteoarthritis ... a form of arthritis in which the cartilages of the joint and the bone adjacent are worn away.

Osteoarthrosis ... chronic non-inflammatory disease of the joints and the bone adjacent (*Chambers*)

All these three are degenerative diseases, usually affecting age groups from 40 upwards. Years ago, the only treatment was medication by drugs (anti-inflammatory drugs like Butizolin, Opren etc.) and they were not very effective. In fact, some were dangerous and even caused death and were eventually withdrawn from the market. The major help now is surgery to replace diseased joints, which has proved to be very successful. A friend of mine had both wrists and knees treated by surgery. The farmer mentioned in a previous chapter had both hip joints replaced, which helped him to carry on running his farm as he had before the arthritis started to trouble him.

Going back 20 years, you could see people crippled by this disease. Then, one of my elderly friends was so crippled, her hands were permanently rigid, her fingers were at right angles to the rest of her hand and her back was bent. She couldn't even hold a cup of tea. She would never complain, but looking at you from under her bent body would say: 'My hands and back are bent, but not my spirit!'

I did not realise that arthritis could affect children, but as I was sitting in my local surgery waiting for my appointment, I read an article written by the publicist Max Clifford about his own daughter, who suffered from arthritis, and his traumatic battles to help this precious child. Unfortunately I was called in for my appointment with the doctor and could not read the article completely and only hope it had a happy ending. I was under the impression that Max Clifford was some sort of agent and having just written my biography, thought he could give me good advice on how to get it published, so I wrote to him and included £50 for his time. The £50 came back plus a very kind letter saying he did not deal in what I asked. Imagine my embarrassment when I saw him on TV some time later and found out he was some very important guru charging not hundreds but thousands of pounds for his services. He must have chuckled at my naivety!

Syphilitic arthritis (a side effect of untreated syphilis). I came across this during my training at King's College hospital during the Second World War. We took over a large mental hospital in Horton near Epsom where we received the wounded from the Middle East. There was one ward left behind with mental patients. Amongst them was one man who had been parachuted with a team of men into France during the First World War. It was said that he had strayed into the naughty red-light district in Paris, where he caught syphilis. He was too ashamed to seek treatment and it turned into arthritic syphilis. All his joints were locked stiff and he was like a plank of wood, shuffling with little steps to move forward. He could not sit down and he ate his food standing up with the help of a nurse. It took three nurses to lift him in and out of the bath. All he could do was either lie down or shuffle along slowly. Of course his disease started before penicillin and he was too far gone by the time it was introduced.

Chapter 41

Concussion

Chambers Dictionary: 'the state of being shaken or jarred; (a state of brief or partial unconsciousness resulting from) a violent blow to the head or neck causing (*usu* temporary) disturbance in brain function'.

Bailliere's Nurses' Dictionary: 'a violent jarring shock to the brain, produced by a fall or blow on the head, characterised by unconsciousness, prostration, pallor, feeble pulse and shallow breathing'.

During my training, a man was brought up from the operating theatre after the investigation of other injuries besides concussion caused by a road accident. He was over 6 foot tall and at least 14 stone in weight. It took four porters to heave him onto the hospital bed. His head touched the top of the bed and his feet the bottom, there was no room for manoeuvre, and he barely fitted in. His modesty was covered only by a white operating gown which had little tags to be tied at the back and he wore the traditional operating theatre socks, which covered his legs up to the knees to keep him warm.

The first hour he lay quite still, then he started to call and moan but no one could understand a word he was saying. The next thing, he started to climb out of bed and cot sides were put in place to stop him. But he still tried to get out of bed, putting his legs over the cot sides, with us nurses trying to restrain him. It was useless, of course. He pushed us away and kicked the cot side, sending it flying and clattering to the floor, then stood up to his full height, swaying back and forth, holding onto the bed with one hand, the other assisting him to pee like Niagara Falls onto the floor. The rest of the patients were craning their necks to see and nurses were scurrying right and left. One was hastily screening the spectacle, another running for a urinal and a third fetching bucket and mop. I stayed with the man and when he had completely relieved himself, as he was standing with his back to his bed, I gave him a good shove into his chest and he duly fell sitting backwards onto his bed. All we had to do then was get his upper body down, lay his head on the pillow and lift his legs and feet back onto the bed. We tucked him in and there he lay, and we heard not another murmur from him to the rest of the day. The poor man had been desperate for the loo and no one understood his hollering. He just could not wet the bed in spite of his concussion; subconsciously he knew he had to get up.

Chapter 42

Spastic (Not Brainless)

Bailliere's Nurses' Dictionary: 'characterised by spastic paralysis (rigidity of muscles)'.

Chambers Dictionary: 'characterized or affected with palsy or spastic paralysis, permanent muscle constriction or involuntary jerky movements caused by injury to the muscle-controlling part of the brain'.

The term 'spastic' in slang is sometimes used for a stupid or useless person and is cruel and thoughtless as a spastic person's brain power is not usually impaired. If parents have a child so affected, a child otherwise quite bright, imagine their anger if the word 'spastic' is used in an insensitive manner. (Nowadays the condition is usually referred to as cerebral palsy.)

My experience of a spastically affected person was Gary, who was fostered as a child and grew up in the same family to manhood, being cared for lovingly by his foster parents. His disability was the left arm and the left leg. He controlled his jerky movements to a large extent and walked with a kind of limp. He was such a likeable lad, with a handsome face and an ever-ready smile, so one forgot his disability. Not only did he grow up to be a charming young man, but he fell in love and married, had two children and even got a job to support his family. He owed his confidence and success in relationships with people entirely to the loving care of his foster parents, my friends, with whom he keeps in touch as if they were his real parents.

A friend of mine told me she was invited to a board meeting for the promotion of a consumer commodity. On each side of the

91

table sat ten people with eyes on the director who presided over the meeting. He was sitting at the top of the table and his secretary sat beside him and took notes. My friend thought there was something not quite right with the director's right arm, but could not make out what. At the end of the meeting they all rose to go to the next room for coffee. The director got up and walked with a kind of jerky limp and my friend realised he had cerebral palsy. This had not stopped him rising to a top position and leading a near-normal life. Later she saw him in the car park entering his chauffeur-driven car.

Chapter 43

Insomnia Versus Sleepiness

Chambers Dictionary: 'sleeplessness; prolonged inability to sleep'.

Everybody must have experienced insomnia some time in their life. Everything from counting sheep to sleeping pills has been tried. The trouble with sleeping pills, which can be so very effective, is that they become addictive. It may take months to come off them. A friend of mine told me that in desperation she bought a tape promising to help her fall asleep without pills. She recounted: 'The tape went like this: "Lie quite still, relax your body. Think you are by the seashore, the waves are lapping gently ... you are relaxed ... you are relaxed ... you feel sleepy... very slee-eepy ... very slee-eepy ... very, very sleeeepy..."' and she went to sleep. Then the tape went off with a loud click and she woke up again. So much for the tape!

I myself must have got up many times in the middle of the night, crept down to the kitchen and heated myself some soup, hoping a full, warm tummy might do the trick. The problem was that by the time I'd warmed the soup, drunk it and cleared up it would be well past midnight, and towards the morning I would fall into a lovely deep sleep when it was nearly time to get up again.

Sleepiness is another matter. The first time I came across it was on night duty at King's College hospital. I would be sitting at the desk with lights subdued. All in the ward would be silent except for a snore or two from the patients. My eyelids would become heavy and start to droop and I would sit up with a start, then my eyelids again would droop and a drowsiness would come over me, and in spite of fighting it I would drop forward onto the desk and

93

wake with a start. Of course the remedy is a cup of coffee, which was always easily available in the ward kitchen.

But this was nothing compared to falling asleep driving in 1980 on the M4 back to Wales from Kent (300 miles). The familiar drowsy feeling and drooping eyelids came over me. Opening windows was of no avail. In desperation I tried to come off the motorway by the old Severn Bridge. I was still fighting my drowsiness. I got onto the exit road behind a Range Rover, which stopped by the roundabout. I must have dropped off just then and went bang into the Range Rover's tow bar. The shock made me wide awake. I had all the damage; the Range Rover had none. The owner came round to see if I was OK, which I was apart from the shock, so I was able to drive home. The owner of the Range Rover never pressed charges; my bill was £750.

This is now a criminal offence. It reminds me of the man who fell asleep at the wheel, careered down onto the railway track in front of an oncoming train and caused carnage. He went to prison. But, by the grace of God, I go free!

Chapter 44

Cancer (The Fearsome One)

Chambers Dictionary: 'loosely, any malignant new growth or tumour; properly, a carcinoma or disorderly growth of epithelial cells which invade adjacent tissues and are frequently spread by the lymphatics and blood vessels to other parts of the body'.

Bailliere's Nurses' Dictionary: 'A general term to describe malignant growths in tissues, of which carcinoma is of epithelial, and sarcoma of connective tissue origin, as in bone and muscle.

1). Scirrhus or hard cancer, usually in the breast.
2). Encephaloid or soft cancer in the internal organs.
3). Epithelial cancer e.g. mouth or lip.'

A cancerous growth is one which is not encapsulated but infiltrates into surrounding tissues, the cells of which it replaces by its own. It is spread by the lymph vessels and causes metastasis (transference of the growth to other parts of the body) if untreated; death is caused by the destruction of organs to a degree incompatible with life. Cancer can lead to extreme debility, anaemia or haemorrhage. The importance of early recognition and treatment cannot be over-emphasised. Surgical removal of the growth and surrounding tissues and lymph glands may be successful. X-ray or radium treatment is advised in some cases. Palliative measures are by operation, such as gastrostomy (partial removal of stomach) colostomy (a surgical formation of a permanent opening into the colon) and gastro-enterostomy (a surgical crossing between the stomach and the small intestine).

Cancer is the most feared disease and top of the yearly death list. Being initially diagnosed as having an unnatural growth, then

95

having to wait an anxious week or so to find out whether it is malignant or not is bad enough, but when eventually it is found to be cancer, the shock and worry begin, prior to the surgery, debilitating chemo-therapy and deep x-ray or radium treatment.

Needless to say, cancer in children is even more tragic, yet it does happen. Somehow these little ones seem to bear the discomfort of the treatment bravely.

As stated, early diagnosis in cancer is essential. The mammograms available now are life-saving. They are provided at either hospitals or in mobile caravan units which visit different districts.

I thought by being a trained nurse I knew all about self-examination, and felt perfectly safe. How wrong I was. I had a very good friend in 1995, a Chinese lady named Lee. As she had no transport at that time I used to take her shopping with me every Thursday. After parking we went past the Town Hall and there was the mammogram caravan. Lee said to me in her broken English, 'You go.'

'Not me, I'm all right, nothing wrong with me,' I said.

'You go,' she insisted.

'All right, just to please you,' I said, and went up the entrance steps into the caravan. Then I saw a notice which said *Women up to 70 years of age*, so I turned round to leave, as I was then over 70, but the nurse stopped me and when I told her my age she said, 'Come in, your age doesn't matter,' and I had the mammogram reluctantly.

Imagine my surprise and worry when a week later I received a letter from the breast clinic in Cardiff to say that I was requested to attend for a needle op as there were suspicious cells. I had the needle op and, after a further wait, unbelievably was in the West Wales hospital for an operation in another week; not a mastectomy but a local lumpectomy, which means they took out the cancerous cell area. I had four weeks of radium treatment followed by Tamoxifen medication for five years, after which I was pronounced cured. Now, another six years later, I'm still free from cancer. This proves how important it is to be diagnosed in the early stages. The mammograms are available free in every district and hopefully women will go to be screened. It might save their lives.

I still wonder why Lee was so insistent that I should be screened. One of those mysteries. Lee has moved away from here but I will always be grateful to her, I dare say she saved my life. If I had waited for a lump to appear, it might have been too late.

Chapter 45

The Jelly Fish Dilemma, or the One That Got Away

Geddes & Crosset Dictionary: 'Jelly fish are sea creatures with a nearly transparent body and long tentacles.'

Chambers Dictionary: '**jellyfish** ... a marine coelenterate [any group of aquatic creatures with a bulbous or tube shaped body and mouth surrounded by tentacles] with jelly-like body'.

A jellyfish is not a fish (John Waters): 'It has no head, no bones, no scales and no fins. It is umbrella shaped or like a bell.'

The river Teifi leads to an estuary out to sea called Llanstephan, approximately 8 miles from Carmarthen. It is like a miniature seaside. An ancient castle towers above the sandy expanse. Robin and I and sometimes our visitors spent many hours exploring the castle ruins, viewing the fantastic sea panorama and recognising Kidwelly across the estuary, then spend time in the coffee shop on the beach, where cream teas, chips and other foods, souvenirs, buckets and spades etc. were available. You can't swim there, because the sand stretches a long way before reaching the water, and even then the water remains very shallow for quite a distance.

The remarkable thing about Llanstephan was that the beach was always covered in jelly fish left stranded by the tide. They seemed to be dotted all over the beach, and one had to be careful not to tread on them. The jelly fish when in water is a most fairylike, near transparent creature with tentacles swaying like delicate lace frills, yet stranded on the beach, completely helpless, motionless, stone grey in colour and the size of a dinner plate it is like an ugly big flat stone. Why these strange creatures got stranded on Llanstephan's beach is a mystery, as I never came across this phenomenon at all the other beaches we went to.

One day when Robin and I were walking on Llanstephan beach, we saw two boys trying to move a jelly fish, maybe back into the water. I went to warn them of the possibility of getting stung. 'And anyway,' I said, 'what difference would it make, to save the one, while there are so many more?'

'It will make a difference to this one,' the boy said.

What wisdom! We did not stay so whether this one was the one that got away, we shall never know.

Chapter 46

Multiple Sclerosis, the Insidious Health Destroyer

Bailliere's Nurses' Dictionary: 'Disseminated (multiple) sclerosis, characterized by hard degenerated patches scattered throughout the nervous system.'

Chambers Dictionary: 'Multiple sclerosis ... a chronic progressive disease in which there is a patchy deterioration of the myelin forming a sheath for the nerve fibres, resulting in various forms of paralysis throughout the body.'

MS, as it is known for short, stretches from onset to final conclusion over many years, sometimes 20 or more. The victim is not aware of its destructive presence for a long time due to its insidious beginning.

The first symptoms are numbness in fingers and toes and not feeling needle pricks, then a slight walking impediment, leading eventually to the need for a wheelchair. This again eventually leads to becoming bed-bound and in need of nursing.

This is a very distressful condition for loving relatives to watch. My own experience of this illness was when district nursing in the 1950s (as reported in my biography). The patient we visited was bedridden, suffering from MS. As an 18-year-old, a lovely, seemingly healthy young girl, she fell in love and married the man of her choice. There were photos displayed of happy holidays, she and her young husband smiling and holding hands. But there were also pictures of the first time the need for the wheelchair became necessary, but again they were still smiling, the husband now standing behind the wheelchair. He pushed her to the shops, on holidays and just for little outings. Now, when we were called in, she was confined to her bed and needed nursing. She was now only 37 years of age. Her husband worked on the London docks and had to get up at five o'clock in the morning to get there. When we nurses arrived to care for his wife, the flat was always spotless. He even left out cups and saucers etc. for tea if it was needed. He still loved her deeply in spite of her illness and all the inconveniences it caused. This was real love, the very deepest kind of love. She used to hum a song to us while we attended to her needs, the song they both loved, the song which apparently brought them together in their courtship. It was called 'My Guy'. This song still lingers in my mind in spite of hearing it those many years ago.

Chapter 47

Stroke

Chambers Dictionary: 'damage to part of the brain, caused by diminished blood flow or leaking of blood through the walls of blood vessels, leading to (often permanent) impairment of sensation, function or movement in those parts controlled by the damaged area'.

Bailliere's Nurses' Dictionary: 'a term to describe a sudden onset of symptoms occurring in cerebral disease e.g. cerebral haemorrhage'.

This dramatic sudden illness is well known and happens sooner or later in many families, usually in the latter years. In my experience and understanding, speech is usually affected, becoming slurred, and paralysis or limited mobility occurs in many cases. Yet very often, after treatment and rest there can be much improvement, and with physiotherapy, many stroke victims regain their speech and walking ability.

Two of my friends were afflicted by sudden strokes. The first, a man in his early seventies, was very badly affected, with loss of speech and loss of walking ability. But after rest and medication he picked up so well he could soon take part again in meetings at church, and he could walk with a walking stick.

Not so my friend Betty. She was a 5-foot-tall, full-of-energy lady. One of our weekly prayer house group members who prayed for other countries in need, she too was in her early seventies. She and Tom her husband lived only a stone's throw from my house, in an ordinary semi-detached, two-bedroom bungalow. They had no children. Then they bought a very lovely new detached two-bedroom house farther down in Merthyr which had a very modern kitchen with white-wood units and all the other new kitchen amenities: an absolute joy for Betty, a dream come true. They were barely there a year when Betty partly collapsed with a stroke and Tom, with help from a neighbour, rushed her to hospital in his car. After seeing her into the ward he returned to their new house and collapsed on the kitchen floor with a fatal heart attack. I don't know who told Betty or how she was told, when she was well enough to understand.

Anyway, Betty was eventually discharged back into her home with the help of Social Services coming in each day. A carer got her up into a wheelchair and gave her breakfast and again put her to bed each night. She had meals on wheels and all the other help available. We all visited her frequently. She seemed to lose weight rapidly and when I asked if she ate her food, she said, 'Yes I do, but I don't eat much, because I don't want to get too heavy for the nurses to lift me when they care for me and have to put me into my wheelchair.' I was amazed at her caring attitude towards those who looked after her. However, she did not seem to improve, unlike my male friend, and eventually she was admitted into an old people's nursing home.

I visited her there and she was only a shadow of her former lively self. On my last visit to her she said to me, 'I'll tell Tom you've been.' She died that same week and all of us who knew her went to her funeral.

Chapter 48

Robin and 'The (Naughty) House
of the Rising Sun'

It was Christmas, a time of good will. The little church held a carol service and there would be a little pantomime played by the children. The usual Christmas carols rang out: 'Silent Night, Holy Night' and 'While Shepherds Watched Their Flocks by Night' etc. Parents were seated waiting eagerly to see their little ones perform on stage. At last the curtain went up. There was a 10-year-old girl as Mary with baby Jesus (a doll), Joseph standing behind Mary and three shepherds, one with his finger up his nose, another grinning and waving at his mum and the third keeping his dignity. They said their lines well and everything went off as planned. The clapping was gratifying.

There were more carols then the leader called out, 'Anyone else wants to recite a poem or sing a song?' And to my surprise Robin put up his hand. The leader went up to him and Robin whispered into his ear. The leader then announced, 'This young man wants to sing a song,' and led him onto the stage. I knew that Robin could sing many ditties which we used to sing at home when I was strumming on the guitar. He had a very good voice and used to sing the hymns in church, too. Today there were all the dignitaries of the church, including the vicar and his wife, and of course all the parents of the children.

So there was Robin on the stage and everybody looking at him expectantly as he started to sing:

There is a house in New Orleans, they call The Rising Sun
It's been the ruin of many poor boy, and Lord I know I'm one.

Eyebrows went up, there was a shuffle of feet and at the back I

103

could hear some titters and suppressed laughter. Robin carried on regardless, and when he got to:

Go tell my baby sister not to do what I have done....

I rushed up to the stage and grabbed him and hauled him off, with him giving me a wounded look, not realising what was wrong. Luckily everybody knew Robin and thought it was a great joke.

Chapter 49

Parkinson's Disease, the Shaking Palsy

Bailliere's Nurses' Dictionary: 'Parkinson's paralysis agitans. It is the sequel to some cases of encephalitis (inflammation of the brain) encephalitis lethargica (sleepy sickness).'

Chambers Dictionary: '**Parkinson's disease** ... shaking palsy; a disease characterized by rigidity, tremor and shaking of hands, etc., studied by James Parkinson (1755–1824).'

It was said by the Schizophrenia Association in Bangor that dopamine, a chemical substance, can cause Parkinson's disease with the typical shaking and tremors of hands etc. if an insufficient quantity passes to the brain, but if too much passes into the brain, mental disturbances (e.g. schizophrenia) can follow. So if medication for mental disturbances is too high, it will give the side effects of Parkinson's disease – shaking of hands, etc. – which can be corrected by modifying the medication. (I hope I have understood this correctly.) I also understand that dopamine is present in some of our food, e.g. soya beans and soya products.

My only experience of this disease was watching a documentary programme on television which was on Parkinson's disease: a shocking eye-opener for people not involved in this terrible illness. Several people took part, including a man and a woman, both in the advanced stages of the disease. Their constant uncontrollable tremors and shaking hands and even jerking heads were distressing to watch. They could not stay still for one moment.

They could not possibly hold a cup of tea, or do any of the simple tasks one has to do daily and does without thinking. Imagine the poor relatives seeing their loved one shaking and trembling all the time, and being helpless and having to do everything constantly for that person, even taking them to the loo. Yes, and trying to feed or spoon-feed in between tremors and shaking, with food spillage all over the place. The nursing carer must have tremendous patience. As for the patient who is suffering, who may have been a very active person in the past, this must be hell on earth for them.

There is medication to minimise the tremors, but no cure. It is a fatal disease and can take years to reach its conclusion.

Chapter 50

Animals and the Disabled

Animals play an important part in the lives of children, the disabled and the aged.

DOGS: to start with the Bernhardiner (St Bernard), this is a very woolly, deep-furred, gentle giant of a dog, used on Swiss mountain rescue, especially for people lost in snowdrifts. He carries a small cask of brandy attached to his collar. When he has sniffed out the lost person he digs the snow around them to expose them, then he lies against them to keep them warm, and they, if they are able, can sip the brandy to revive themselves. Then this lovely dog starts to howl, a long mournful eerie sound which can be heard miles away and brings the rescue team to the lost victim. We all know the great importance of the guide dog for the blind and some other immobilising disabilities. Then there are the cleverly trained dogs the police use to catch criminals and sniff out illegal drugs. And lastly the dear loyal companionship of a beloved dog to young and old alike.

GOATS: They can be very cantankerous. My first experience, told to me by my sister, as I was only two years old, was of the family pet goat. I was sitting near a pond when he charged, butted me in the back and pushed me into the lake. Luckily my sister saw it and came to the rescue. In spite of this I still liked the creatures and could milk a goat when 10 years old. I remember the time when my father took a goat kid down the cellar to kill it. After half an hour he came up, hugging the kid to his chest, and said, 'I just couldn't do it, it was the way the kid looked at me.'

HORSES: My first encounter was when I came as an au pair to a couple to care for their two-year-old child Patricia. I would take her for little walks. There was a field nearby where we used to admire a horse and touch his soft nose and fondle it, giving it lumps of sugar. One day we went and there was a very young foal in the field which we hadn't seen before. Surely it must have been born only yesterday. I wanted so much to stroke this lovely young thing and show it to Patricia. There was a small gap in the fence just big enough for us to squeeze in. So in we went and slowly advanced to the foal so as not to frighten it away. Suddenly the mare appeared – I presumed it was the mare – as from nowhere. She came at a steady trot, making a beeline for me. There was no mistake. I stopped, mesmerised, not knowing whether to turn and run, but I had the little child clinging to my hand. The mare came towards me and gently put her nose onto my chest and started to push me slowly backwards to where we had entered. It was so slowly that I could easily walk backwards without tripping. I was in panic and fear and when we got to the gap in the fence I pushed Patricia out first then followed. Then the mare turned and went back to her foal. I realised all she wanted to do was to get us away from her foal and meant no harm to us; also, she seemed to recognise Patricia as being a youngster like her foal. Never again did I approach a baby animal with a mother near by.

My next encounter was when training as a nurse in the King's College Hospital sector near Epsom. We were allowed in our off-duty time to ride the horses from a nearby stable. So we went in a group. As I had not had any instruction in riding, the owner allocated me a very gentle, mild horse and said, 'You'll be all right with him, just sit still and don't use your spurs.' I sat bravely and off we trotted. All went well for about half a mile, then my horse suddenly turned round and galloped all the way back to his stable with me clinging on for dear life with my arms round his neck and heart pounding. Back at the stable he shook himself violently and me right off, into the astounded owner's arms. The owner apologised, saying, 'You must have passed your tension and nervousness to him and he felt the best thing to do was return to the stable.'

My only other riding experiences were riding with the disabled through lovely countryside, woodlands and by babbling little brooks.

HAMSTERS: We kept a golden hamster when the girls were seven and nine years old. We called him – I think it was a he – Goldy.

The girls kept him in his cage in their bedroom. Unfortunately one day the cage door wasn't shut properly and Goldy went on a tour of the house. We could not find him anywhere. Eventually on the second day in the evening, the girls were just about to go to bed when they claimed they heard him squeaking behind the bedroom wall. This being a double cavity wall, he must have been caught there. How he got in is a mystery. Maybe from the bathroom, where pipes led out through the wall and did not fit perfectly. Anyway, there arose a wail of sorrow from the girls: 'Please, mum, help...' The squealing went on. The girls wept. As I saw it, the only way was to knock a hole into the wall. 'You can always cover it up afterwards with wallpaper,' said my oldest daughter helpfully. I knocked a hole into this brick wall, sweating from the hard labour, and then we tied nylon tights together, like they do in films with sheets to escape from windows. We let this device down the hole and waited... 'Look, mum,' the girls shrieked as the bit of nylon tights they held seemed to tremble. And would you believe it, up came Goldy out of the hole and scuttled straight back into his cage. But what actually came up and out of the hole wasn't like Goldy, but a black dirty rat-like creature. Poor Goldy, out of the dungeons. Then we witnessed the most amazing performance. The first thing Goldy did was rush into his open cage and drink and drink ... then rush around squeaking in delight, then rush around again, like a joyful dance. We could hardly believe the relief and joy and happiness this little creature displayed at being rescued. After this, it took three days of grooming and preening himself before Goldy became clean again and like our Goldy.

SHEEP: Sheep roamed and grazed freely in the Forest of Dean. But should a sheep stray into your garden, there was a law that either the owner of the sheep paid you compensation for damage caused, or, if you had not heard from him within three weeks, you could keep the sheep. One morning to my horror I saw a sheep trampling and feeding in my vegetable garden. Someone had left the gate open. I went to catch the sheep and lo ... it had only three legs and it was easy to get hold of it. So I tied it on a very long rope to the gate post outside the cottage so it could graze on the grass on the forest side but not escape. Because it had lost one leg we felt sorry for this sheep and we called it Lizy. I found

109

out which farmer it belonged to and phoned him to compensate me for the damage caused and collect his sheep. He duly came and when he saw the sheep had only three legs he said, 'You can keep the sheep,' and he drove off in his Range Rover So here we were with a three-legged sheep. And as much as we liked Lizy, we couldn't possibly keep her, so we let her loose to roam the forest as she had done before. She must have liked us because she came often to visit us and we would stroke her and let her go again.

Here in Merthyr we have sheep grazing at the back of our house on the hill. During the time when we owned a dog, I used to feed dog biscuits to the sheep. They got to know me and I had only to come out of the back door and they would all come running down the hill for their biscuits. Once a mongrel dog chased the sheep and got hold of one. My neighbours and I shouted at the dog to let go, and a man climbed over the fence and beat it off with a stick. The poor sheep was bleeding from an ear where the dog had tried to drag it along. We phoned the farmer, who came and picked up the sheep in his arms like a baby and took it away. The police were informed but I don't know what happened to the dog.

CATS: I lost both Sarah and Ginger, but both lived to be 18 years old. When I was 80 years old, I felt to get another pet was unfair. If anything happened to me I would hate to think it might be put down. So imagine my surprise when one of my neighbour's cats, Felix, seemed to take to me. He spends most of his time in my house. But he has a later chapter to himself.

HEDGEHOGS: We once had a family of hedgehogs, parents and three young visiting our garden in the evenings. They were delightful to watch. Sadly, when we built a wall to replace a fallen-down fence they never came again. I have been told they don't like walls.

BEES: When I had my three beehives in the Forest of Dean, I was told by an experienced bee-keeper that if anything dramatic happens in a family like a birth, wedding, or funeral, go tell the bees. Which I did!

Chapter 51

Coeliac Disease

Chambers Dictionary: 'a condition of the intestines in which a sensitivity to gluten prevents the proper absorption of nutrients (also called **gluten enteropathy**)'.

Bailliere's Nurses' Dictionary: '... also known as pancreatic infantilism. There is a congenital inability to absorb fats which are however split up. Careful diet, excluding fats until about the age of six, may result in restoration of normal function'.

Either the condition described in the *Nurses' Dictionary* is a separate one to the coeliac we know now to be due to gluten sensitivity or, all those years ago (1940) the condition had not been fully recognised or investigated.

Coeliac disease seems to be more prevalent in children, yet adults too can suffer from it. Usually a biopsy of the intestine is necessary, generally after the person has been suffering from diarrhoea for a long time. We all suffer from diarrhoea occasionally but this does not mean we have got coeliac disease. Only after different treatments have been tried for diarrhoea will the doctor come to the conclusion it could be coeliac disease and order the biopsy, which is the only thing confirming the diagnosis.

One of my best friends suffered for months on and off with stomach upset, diarrhoea and sickness before coeliac disease was suspected and she had the intestine biopsy which confirmed it. A gluten-free diet was recommended and the moment she was on it her health improved dramatically. Sadly the time which elapses between the time of constant suffering and eventual diagnosis can be very distressing to the sufferer, especially little children.

111

Gluten is present in bread, cakes, biscuits and any other wheat product. Many shops have gluten-free goods and also mark other food as either gluten-free or not. Some superstores have whole shelves with gluten-free biscuits, cakes, soups and other foods. Coeliac sufferers can obtain a prescription for gluten-free bread and gluten-free flour. Maize flour (sometimes marked as corn flour) can be used instead and cornflakes are fine. But beware of commercial soups, gravies, custards, puddings and sauces in restaurants, as they may all contain flour.

Chapter 52

Skin Invaders

DERMATITIS

> *Bailliere's Nurses' Dictionary*: 'inflammation of the skin, seborrhoea (excessive discharge from sebaceous glands) due to infection by the staphylococcus and the bottle bacillus. Flannel rash is a form of this.'

> *Chambers Dictionary*: 'an inflammation of the skin'.

In my experience both this disease and eczema are very painful, unsightly, itchy and irritating, with a desperate want to scratch, which of course would worsen the condition. An adult can control this urge, but not a child. Imagine a child suffering with either of these diseases and the harassed parent trying to stop their child from scratching. And imagine the child's reaction at other children recoiling at the unpleasant sight of this skin disease thinking they might catch it, when it is actually non-contagious.

ERYTHEMA

> *Bailliere's Nurses' Dictionary*: 'a superficial inflammation of the skin, occurring in red patches of variable size and shape; it is not contagious. E. nodosum, an inflammatory patchiness of the skin with raised, round erythematous nodules, sometimes indicative of a sub-acute rheumatic infection'.

> *Chambers Dictionary*: 'redness of the skin'.

During my training at King's College hospital one of our nurses had this condition. It did not hurt, It did not irritate or itch, but it

113

was just so very unsightly, e.g. red patches showing on her arms and legs which she tried to hide. She used to chew sunflower seeds, having been told it would cure it. I have never since seen this condition again.

ECZEMA

Bailliere's Nurses' Dictionary: 'an acute or chronic inflammatory condition of the skin. It is non-infectious, although secondary infection is common. External irritants may cause it e.g. washer woman eczema (soap suds) baker's eczema (flour) or is sometimes due to certain proteins. Infantile eczema which occurs during the six month–two year period. In eczema an eruption appears first with papules which become moist (weeping) and finally form scabs. There is great irritation of the affected part.

Chambers Dictionary: 'a skin disease in which part of the skin is red, with numerous small papules that turn into vesicles'.

ERYSIPELAS

Bailliere's Nurses' Dictionary: 'an acute contagious disease caused by the streptococcus erysipelas's and characterized by localized inflammation of the skin with pain and fever. The inflammation always commences around a wound, sometimes too small to be apparent and appears in the form of a raised red rash with small blebs spreading gradually from the centre and having a well defined margin. Considerable oedema occurs if near loose tissues, e.g. eyes or scrotum. The onset of the disease is severe accompanied by rigors, vomiting, and sudden rise in temperature. Facial erysipelas is especially dangerous to the possibility of cavernous sinus infection by the veins, giving rise to meningitis. Today antibiotics will cure the condition dramatically.'

Chambers Dictionary: 'an inflammatory disease, generally in the face, marked by a redness of the skin'.

I remember years ago in hospital, a woman was admitted with her poor face swollen like a balloon, all puffed up, eyes hardly visible.

114

All they found was a small cut which had become infected and within 24 hours her face was unrecognisable. Now antibiotics cure this condition in a dramatic way.

SKIN CANCER: See Chapter 111.

Chapter 53

The Joy of Camping

In 1967 while we were still living in Chigwell, I decided to take my two boys, Christopher aged 14 and Robin aged 12 – the girls had left home by then – on a camping holiday in Switzerland.

On hindsight I am now amazed how I and two young boys managed in our old Vauxhall car to carry a tent, a double-tier bunk camp bed (for the boys), a single camp bed for myself, a folding table, three folding chairs (on the roof rack) three sleeping bags, three pillows, a picnic basket with plates, cups and cutlery, one small saucepan, one small frying pan and extra food like tins of baked beans, cereals, bread, butter and long-life milk, along with clothes, swimming gear and towels.

We set out with an AA supportive road map. Robin in spite of his disability was the main navigator as he loved reading road signs. Christopher wrote down all the places we passed.

Our first stop was down in Kent with relations. Then on to Folkestone and the Channel ferry to Zeebrugge, a wondrous experiment for the boys, who relished exploring the upper deck of the ship, watching the English coast disappear and the white waves splashing against the boat sides, then rushing downstairs to the machine room and watching the huge engine turbines in full swing.

On the other side of the Channel after disembarking we drove through Brussels and about a mile out of this city we found a place with pine trees, where we stopped to have some refreshments. I cooked baked beans and fried bread on our little camping gas stove, which tasted delicious in the fresh air with us being very hungry. We then drove across Belgium into Germany and on to their miles-long autobahn. We only stopped once overnight in a German youth hostel, which was all built in pinewood, a fabulous place.

116

From there we drove down the autobahn right up to Switzerland and Basel. My next relations, a nephew and his wife, lived only about 10 miles from Basel. So this was our next stop for rest and refurbishments of our belongings. We had a lovely reunion with them and were sorry to leave again the next day as we had arranged to be at my sister's in Brig in the Bernese Oberland (Alps).

So then we drove over mountains to get to our destination and another happy family reunion. We all decided to spend 10 days at an Italian Riviera camp site. So my sister and brother-in-law packed their camping equipment into their car and together we drove through the Simplon Tunnel, which leads through the mountains into Italy. We visited Florence and could still see the marks 6 feet high on buildings caused by the floods the previous year. We also saw the leaning tower of Pisa and marvelled at it standing without falling.

We eventually got to the Riviera camp site near Livorno and set up camp to stay for 10 days. To our surprise we were right next door to the bandstand where they played late into the night. One of the then popular songs, from what I remember, went like this: 'Volare oh ... oh ... Cantare oh ... oh ... oh ... oh.' We got used to it and didn't mind. We spent a lovely time there, swimming and sunbathing with the boys. Robin, who can swim, enjoyed the warm sea.

The only outing we took part in was to the island of Elba, where Napoleon had been exiled. The house he had been allocated was on top of a hill with fantastic views right down over the whole island and the surrounding sea. This lovely holiday came to an end and we said goodbye to my sister and brother-in-law. My sister took the high road back to Switzerland and we took the low road home via France. Grapes were in season and practically given away. To our enjoyment we had grapes with every meal. The last camp was near Paris. My memory there was getting up early for hot buttered croissants for breakfast. Lastly back to Dunkirk, across the Channel and home after three weeks of sunshine holidays. Apparently the day after our return there were storms and winds which caused havoc on the Channel crossing. Cars got damaged bumping into each other on the windswept ferry. We missed this by just one day.

Our next camping holiday was in Devonshire the next year. The weather was bad and winds shook our tent and we had to hang on for dear life to the frames to keep it from being swept away. All our clothes and bedding were constantly damp. It was a nightmare. No way would I want to experience this again. I then sold the tent.

Chapter 54

The Common Cold, Hay Fever and Influenza

THE COMMON COLD (usually a winter invader)

Bailliere's Nurses' Dictionary: '**the common cold (catarrh)** inflammation of a mucous membrane e.g., naso-pharynx accompanied by discharge of mucus. Catarrh may be chronic in which case there is little or no inflammation'.

Chambers Dictionary: '**catarrh** ... a discharge of fluid resulting from the inflammation of a mucous membrane, *esp* of the nose'.

INFLUENZA (the endemic winter invader)

Bailliere's Nurses' Dictionary: 'an endemic form of catarrh inflammation affecting the alimentary or respiratory tract. It is accompanied by fever, pain in the limbs and occasionally by complications such as pleurisy and pneumonia. When the fever has passed extreme prostration follows, and convalescence must be carefully guarded against relapse. Mental depression is frequently a complication after an attack'.

Chambers Dictionary: 'a highly contagious viral infection characterized by headache, fever, muscular aches and pains and inflammation of the respiratory passages'.

HAY FEVER (the pollen misery)

Bailliere's Nurses' Dictionary: 'an acute catarrh affecting the nasal mucous membrane and the conjunctiva, and caused by the pollen of grasses etc. (an allergic disease)'.

Chambers Dictionary: 'irritation by pollen of the nose, throat etc, with sneezing and headache'.

Only people who have suffered any of these diseases know the misery and distress they cause. Whereas the common cold is usually of short duration, influenza is the more serious disease and can even kill the elderly or weak. A winter disease, immunisation is strongly recommended in autumn. The year when an influenza epidemic came from Japan, killing hundreds of people in its path was a grim reminder of this sometimes yearly recurring winter disease. Both the common cold and influenza are contagious.

Hay fever is not infectious but a seasonal visitor to the poor person allergic to pollen. It can cause the same misery as a common cold. Some years the pollen count is higher than others. There are now pollen counts given on TV to warn people of the severity of pollen in the air.

Chapter 55

Cave Dwellers

When Robin was 16 years old we joined my oldest daughter Jennifer and her family for a holiday in Majorca. Apart from the usual happy holiday activities, we decided one day to explore the island and we hired two cars, one for Jennifer and her family and one for myself and Robin. We were warned to remain only on the main road up the mountains, as in outlying places lived rough people, brigands and such. There had been stories of people and their cars mysteriously disappearing and were never being heard of or found again.

The day we chose was a lovely hot day and I followed Jenn's and Pete's car till we got to a crossroads where another car got in between us and I lost our leading car completely. I drove on, hopefully in the right direction, to the next crossroads. There were signs but in Spanish, which neither Robin nor I could understand. So I drove on and on and the road got narrower and narrower. We turned back to the crossroads and tried the other route. But again this road got narrower and narrower, leading further up the mountains.

We stopped to try and reassess our position when I noticed a few yards above on the grassy ground by the rock face, an antenna sticking up into the sky next to what appeared to be a dark opening in the rock face. This was not the only antenna, there were several more dotted here and there coming out near the rock face. There seemed a rough path leading up to the nearest one. Frustrated and near to tears, Robin and I went up to investigate. As we got near it a dark-haired man stood in the opening of what we now realised was a cave in the mountain. Not only was it a cave, but actually a cave dwelling.

The man stood staring at me in a menacing, hooded sort of way. A woman appeared behind him. I didn't know whether to turn and run or remain. So I stood there completely still, mesmerised. Then Robin did what he always did (not fearing or aware of any danger) – he smiled and held out his hand to the woman, who took it and they shook hands, then Robin held his hand out to the man, who looked at it with knitted eye brows until the woman gave him a push in the ribs with her elbow as if to say 'go on'. Then his shifty face suddenly cracked into a big grin, he took Robin's hand and shook it as though they were old friends. The ice was broken.

The woman motioned us into their cave dwelling and we were amazed at the comfort inside. The cave walls had been covered with tiles. There were chairs and a table and easy chairs and a television set in the corner (hence the antenna). So we realised that all those other antennas belonged to other cave dwellers. There were no windows in this cave but they had electricity, which the men had led up in coils from I don't know where. Presumably deeper in the cave must have been a cooking place and sleeping areas. They sat us in chairs by the table and offered us a drink, which we gladly accepted. There then came one of those difficult times trying to communicate by signs. I think the woman understood our problem and since the firm's telephone number of our hired car was displayed on the car, the man, after an argument with the woman, wrote it down on a piece of paper and cycled off, I presume to somewhere where a telephone was available.

We spent another hour with these cave people and were introduced to their five lovely dark-eyed children. At last, another car from the same firm appeared with two men. One jumped out of the car and the other drove off hell for leather. The man left behind would not come up to the cave but shouted for us to come down. We did, and he practically shoved us into the car, slammed the door and drove off as though the devil was behind him and didn't stop for a hair-raising mile. When we came to a kind of plateau he stopped and wiped the sweat off his brow with his handkerchief, gave a deep sigh and looked at me, shaking his head, and said; 'Did no one tell you not to venture up there?' This apparently was the place of robbers, brigands etc.

Was it Robin who saved the day? Or did the woman recognise Robin's disability? And no way would these people rob the disabled and a single woman in distress. When we got back we were surrounded by holiday people asking us all about the cave people and how we had got away unscathed.

Chapter 56

The Heart

Bailliere's Nurses' Dictionary: 'a muscular organ which pumps the blood throughout the body, it is situated behind the sternum, slightly towards the left side of the thorax. It is divided into four chambers, connected by valves. The two upper chambers are called auricles and the two lower ventricles. Out of the left ventricle arises the aorta or main artery of the body.'

Chambers Dictionary: 'the organ that circulates the blood throughout the body ... the innermost part; the core; the chief or vital part; the breast, bosom; the (imagined) place of origin of the affections, understanding and thought, as opposed to the head, the seat of reason, courage, innermost feelings or convictions; vigour, spirit; cordiality; compassion'.

Heart Disease (the feared one)

My own experience of heart malfunction was in 2003 when one morning as I got up, I suddenly had to gasp for breath, experiencing panic and fear of death. Luckily my daughter and son-in-law happened to be staying with me at that time and called the emergency services. The paramedics were in my bedroom it seemed within 10 minutes and clasped an oxygen mask over my nose, which immediately eased the breathing. I was rushed to hospital and diagnosed as having a faulty heart valve which could be replaced by a pig's heart valve (poor pig). Being then 85 years of age, a risk was involved. I felt I had to take this risk since without it I would have to live with an oxygen mask attached to my face for the rest of my life. Once in Morriston hospital where the operation was to take place, they wasted no time. I went down to the operating theatre next morning at 7 a.m. I was back in the ward and waking up at 1 p.m. My daughter and son-in-law were waiting at my bedside. Only just coming round, I was confused and thought it was 1 a.m. and said to them, 'What on earth are you two doing here at this time of night? I'm still waiting to go down for the operation.'

'Mum, you've had the operation.'

It was only then I realised I was trussed up like a chicken but was breathing without oxygen. I was only one week in intensive care, then transferred for convalescence in another small hospital near my home.

After heart surgery most people are put on warfarin medication to stop the blood from clotting. You go to the special clinic for frequent blood tests to make sure the blood is at the right level of anti-clotting. This clinic, I found, was always full of people who had had life-prolonging heart surgery like myself. Today's modern treatment and heart transplant surgery has improved and saved many lives. There were people there who had had pacemakers, heart valve replacements, and heart by-passes to correct heart problems. I was one of many, to my surprise.

Heart Transplants

The first heart transplant was performed in Cape Town, South Africa, at the Groote Schuur hospital by surgeon Christiaan Barnard on 3rd December 1967. Christiaan Barnard was born in 1922, his father a minister of the church. He studied medicine and surgery at Cape Town University. One of his brothers, much mourned by his father, died of heart disease which could have been operated on with today's surgery. Was this the reason Christiaan Barnard was stirred in this direction?

Before this, the first heart transplant, there were many delays and disappointments waiting for a donor. Already a possible donor had been lost and the willing receiving patient, Louis Washkansky, who was 53, was getting nearer and nearer to death with a very diseased heart. A 25-year-old girl was fatally injured and her mother killed outright. The girl was brought into hospital. The only survivor, the father, Edward George Darvall, now had the dramatic, awful

125

decision put to him, would he allow his daughter's heart to give life to another human being? Christiaan Barnard himself did the asking. And Edward Darvall gave consent. Did he give this decision because of the tragic loss of both his beloved daughter and wife, he hoped that his daughter's heart would go on beating in another human being in need and so leaving a life force of his lost family behind?

In Christiaan Barnard's book *One Life*, published by George G. Harrap & Co. Ltd., he tells how deeply and seriously he took the life-giving surgery he performed. He says he prays before every operation. And he gives the prayer he prayed before his so dramatic first heart transplant, not knowing what might happen and not being totally confident of success.

Oh Lord please guide my hands to keep them free from error.
As you have freed me from doubt,
Show me the way to do this as well as I can.
To this, for this man who has placed his life into my hands...
And for all other men like him and all others on the team
That they may also be with us every minute of the way.
Amen.

Chapter 57

Robin in Action

At home Robin was always very helpful. He could peel potatoes, help to dry crockery and put it away, make his own bed and even mow the lawn with the electric hover lawn mower, but all this only after I had shown him how. As mentioned before, he is excellent at navigating and on holiday likes swimming and walking. He used to race around on his bicycle using all the needed hand signals for safety and I think might have done cycle racing with a club had he been OK. He beat almost everybody at table tennis and is very good at playing Scrabble. In spite of his diminished reading understanding, his spelling is excellent, but his handwriting has deteriorated to an unreadable scribble. As a rule he behaves well when in company and can be taken out to restaurants and other places of amusements, providing he has not had anything to upset him food wise. Some of the boys in Longford Court, where Robin is now, seem so very autistic and even disturbed I wonder how staff manage them on their frequent outings, and how they get them to do gardening etc. Yet they do just that.

All the holidays I've taken Robin on have been enjoyable and without disturbed incidents. The last two-week holiday I had with him was in Cyprus. This was during the time he was in Cwm Celyn nursing home in Blaina, the third and last home before joining Longford Court. It was at this home where they accused him of being aggressive and destructive, yet we had a wonderful stress-free holiday and had our meals in the Holiday Inn and mingled with the other holiday people by the swimming pool and went on other outings without problems.

Robin would do some strange things if he was disturbed and always the reason was that I had not taken good care about a sweet or ice-cream being suitable. Like when we went to our little St Luke's church, where there were refreshments before the service. It was Robin's birthday and I had invited two of the congregation to a meal out to celebrate with Robin after the service. People were sitting by tables in the church hall with their tea/coffee mugs now empty on the tables. Robin suddenly got up and went from table to table, picked a mug up at a time and just dropped it on the floor. People were watching mesmerised, and I was trailing after him, pleading: 'Robin, don't. Please don't.' But he just carried on. There was no aggression and, strangely, none of the mugs broke, to the wonder of us all. So I took Robin home before the service started and my two friends said they would come to my house after it had finished to decide what we would do. The restaurant dinner was off.

When I got home and asked Robin why he behaved this way in church, he gave his usual reply whenever he was disturbed: 'I didn't feel well', and he went to bed. I duly prepared some food at home which was ready when my two friends arrived. It was only a simple meal but we enjoyed it just the same. So this is how Robin's birthday was celebrated that year, he in bed, me with two friends downstairs having a make-shift meal.

Chapter 58

Migraine

Bailliere's Nurses' Dictionary: 'a neurosis manifested by periodic attacks of severe headaches, often one sided and accompanied by vertigo (giddiness, loss of equilibrium) vomiting and disturbance of vision'.

Chambers Dictionary: 'a severe throbbing pain affecting only one half of the head or the face and usually accompanied by nausea'.

This must be one of the most disabling, painful conditions. It is not disfiguring, it is not fatal, but the pain is excruciating and only the strongest pain killers will touch it. To carry out an occupation is impossible during an attack. Some may be of short duration, others may go on for days. Some people have suffered these attacks for years.

There was a report in the national press of a lady who suffered migraine on and off for many years. It occurred so often she worried even when well, thinking, 'When will the next attack come? When, how ... and where...?' She heard of a lady in Wales who recommended a herb which she claimed would cure migraine. Clutching at straws, she wrote in desperation, pleading with this lady to help and give her the name of the miracle herb.

The Welsh lady told her that feverfew (a European herb formerly used to reduce fevers) should help her, perhaps even cure her. She should be able to purchase the feverfew herb at any health shop and she should prepare it like ordinary tea: put the herb into the tea pot and pour boiling water over it, let it stand five minutes to infuse, and, if liked, sweeten it with a little honey. It would make a delicious drink, apart from its healing properties.

This lady claimed with great joy that the painful migraines got less and less and finally did not occur again. So feverfew has been recommended as a cure for migraine. It is only one of many herbs with healing properties. And drug companies have been using herbs to make some of their curing drugs by extracting the healing factors from the herbs and putting them into tablet form, or in oils to rub into the skin as in aromatherapy.

So this migraine story had a happy ending. Hopefully all migraine sufferers will have the same good result with feverfew.

Chapter 59

Fear: The Gripping Terror

Chambers Dictionary: 'a painful emotion excited by danger; apprehension of danger or pain; alarm; solitude; anxiety; that which causes alarm; risk or possibility; reverence or awe (*relig*) ... *vt* to regard with fear, be afraid of: to expect with alarm; to be regretfully inclined to think; to revere (*relig*) ... to make afraid; *vi* to be afraid; to suspect some danger ... to be in doubt'.

Real fear can grip you like a steel clamp tightening on your heart. The little mouse in front of the snake's piercing eyes, completely mesmerised, not able to move, is in fear, awaiting certain death.

One of my fearful encounters was years ago. We had a caravan holiday in Hastings near the sea, just myself and my four children, the youngest, Robin, then 5 years old and Jennifer, the oldest, 14, while Chris was 7 and Pat 12. We'd had a lovely day by the sea playing ball and swimming. After tea the evening was still pleasant and we decided to go for a walk along the cliffs, on a fairly narrow path. The views were fabulous. We walked on and on and suddenly we came to a part which could not be negotiated, so we went back a little and tried another route. By now it was getting dark and I began to worry as visibility diminished and we were near the cliffs, a possible 100-foot fall if we made a mistake. There was now a mist, which made my sandals wet and slippery, and I took them off as my feet seemed to slide in them. So I was barefoot. Robin was tired and Jennifer took him and carried him piggy-back, and Pat held Christopher's hand. So on we marched, by now with the mist upon us a very miserable little band. There for the first time I experienced real deep fear, fear for the children. We were near a

131

dangerously high cliff, we were lost and I had no clue which way to go. Worse, no one knew we were there. We had told no one where we were going that evening. As far as our neighbours knew, we were in our caravan. I panicked, but Jennifer kept her head and took over, a mere 14-year-old girl. With Robin on her back she said bravely, 'Don't worry mum, just follow me.' We did, one behind the other, with Jennifer in the lead taking us slowly step by step hopefully in the right direction.

After a while, 'I see a light!' shouted Chris, and there it was, not too far away. We made for it, and it turned out to be a cottage. I knocked on the door and a friendly man looked us over, four children, wet and bedraggled, and me nearly in tears. He knew our caravan site and led us back. How thankful we were. Never again did I venture along paths unknown.

Another fearful experience came when I was training at King's College hospital. I made friends with a married couple living almost opposite the hospital. They had a second-hand shop and owned a caravan by the Thames near Richmond, which they allowed me to go to for weekends with another nurse. I had been there often, enjoying the river and the surroundings. This time, however, the nurse who was to accompany me was recalled to duty at the last minute and could not come. It was now too late for me to find someone else and I decided to go on my own. I got to the caravan late in the evening, had a snack, then went to bed. This caravan was in a field all by itself. Everything was peaceful and quiet and I went to sleep. Then I was wakened by stamping outside the caravan. It must have been past midnight. I did not dare put on a light and guessed the time. I sat up, not daring to breathe. Was I hearing right, or was it my imagination, that something was trying the caravan door? The stamping or heavy footsteps went on round the caravan. My inner fear at being there alone was becoming a nightmare. I hid under the bedclothes waiting for something terrible to happen, trembling and shaking for what seemed an eternity. The stamping stopped and I don't know whether the silence was even more ominous. At last morning came and I peered out from behind the curtain: there was nothing there now, just the field around me. I could not eat anything, I seemed to be still in shock after the night's fearful stamping, so I went miserably down to the river's edge and sat with my head in my hands.

'Hello, what have we here?' It was a man who had just embarked from his boat. He seemed so kind and friendly that I told him of my horrible experience of the past night and that I was a nurse in training at King's College hospital. He said: 'You look all done in. Come on my boat and I'll give you some breakfast and take you for a ride up river and you'll forget all about it.' I gladly accepted and spent the morning in this man's company. At midday he suggested I could spend the weekend with him as I would not spend another night in the caravan alone. I thanked him but wanted to get back to the hospital, and he kindly took me and my suitcase back to the station and even arranged to stay there until the train was due. I could not thank him enough for all the kind help he had given me. Needless to say, I would never, ever, stay on my own in another caravan.

One of the most fearful experiences, as told me by a mountaineer, is to be caught high up on a mountain in a storm. The sound of thunder and lightning is frightening when you are in your own home, but out on a mountain, miles from home or civilisation, open to gale-force winds and the roaring thunder echoing back and forth from mountain to mountain, cracking like gunshots against the cliffs, shaking your very soul, is an experience never to be forgotten and leaves you with awe at the power of nature for the rest of your life.

Fear can be the most disabling experience. Real fear can shatter your senses into immobility, like the little mouse hypnotised and mesmerised by the snake.

The strange thing is, Robin and other autistic people do not seem to experience fear. Part of autism is having stunted feelings. So an autistic person is not aware of dancer. One of the main reasons they need to be cared for.

Chapter 60

Cretinism Versus Goitre

CRETINISM

Bailliere's Nurses' Dictionary: '**Cretinism** is a congenital disease, characterized by absence of the thyroid gland, thickness of neck, stunted growth, and imperfect mental faculties. It is common in the Swiss Alps.'

Chambers Dictionary: '**cretin** ... a child suffering from a congenital deficiency of thyroxine (thyroid hormone) which, if untreated, can lead to mental retardation and incomplete physical development'.

GOITRE

Bailliere's Nurses' Dictionary: 'an enlargement of the thyroid gland, causing a marked swelling in front of the neck which sometimes causes pressure on the trachea. It may be endemic in the British Isles. Derbyshire neck is of this type.'

Chambers Dictionary: 'abnormal enlargement of the thyroid gland, producing a swelling in front of the throat, sometimes accompanied by exophthalmus [abnormal protrusion of the eyeballs]'.

I find it interesting that the *Nurses' Dictionary* mentions cretinism as being common in the Swiss Alps. So is the goitre condition. I remember seeing many farmers living in the Alps with these huge goitres (growths) on their necks just below the chin, and just as many stunted men (cretinism). And women were affected as well. Years ago lack of iodine – which is contained in salt-water fish –

134

was blamed. As a child in school I was given one iodine tablet (I can't remember if daily or weekly) with the rest of the children, implemented by the government to stop this endemic condition. Of course now with the huge refrigerating lorries bringing seafood into Switzerland, goitre and cretinism have disappeared and iodine tablets in school are no longer necessary, seafood containing iodine is on the menu now in Switzerland as abundantly as in Britain.

These goitres did not seem to cause pain nor were they fatal – in other words, they were non-malignant – but they could cause breathing difficulties by pressing on the trachea. I remember this condition as a child in the 1920s and of course it had then been known for many years.

Chapter 61

Mad Cow Disease (BSE)

Not mentioned in my 1940 *Bailliere's Nurses' Dictionary*; obviously did not exist then, when cattle were only fed on grass and hay, their natural food.

Chambers Dictionary: '**bovine spongiform encephalopathy** ... an infectious degenerative brain disease of cattle ... *orig* caused by cattle feed processed from scrapie-infected sheep remains'.

By the folly of man, this deadly cattle disease is passed to humans through the food chain. Apparently the incubation period can be anything up to 10 years, and we still don't know when the last case will establish itself. According to some reports there may be many more cases incubating without symptoms at present.

We have all seen on TV the afflicted cow doddering, then falling and trying vainly to get up but falling back completely. The obvious had happened. On investigation including blood samples BSE was diagnosed. The animal had to be put down. Were these animal carcasses burned as the law demands or did some of it find its way into the food chain? Or did young calves, unknown to the farmer, already carry the deadly virus from their infected mothers and were then sold as veal?

The very sad part is that it seems many young people have been affected by VCJD, the human equivalent. The kind of youngsters who love meeting in burger bars and socialising. Where did they pick up this distressing deadly bug? Were they in their own home or out clubbing?

Only parents who have lost their son or daughter to this deadly disease know the fear and misery of watching while a beloved child slowly dies before their very eyes, with no hope of a cure: a young person who had been so full of energy and enjoyment, and a happy life ahead of them. Several cases were publicised on TV. It was distressing even to watch parents standing by the bedside of their daughter or son so afflicted, feeling completely helpless.

There was a programme which claimed that this disease had been found in cannibal tribes. Does this mean grass-eating animals shouldn't be fed other animals' carcasses even when not infected? Whatever, let's hope this cattle disease will never enter the human chain food again.

Chapter 62

Robin at Risk

We had been in Llechryd for eight years. Up to now Robin and I seemed to go on happily day by day. As I mentioned in Chapter 20, I was doing voluntary car service, taking patients to hospital appointments and back, which I enjoyed, while Robin was being taken to occupational therapy in Newcastle Emlyn, taking with him food I had prepared, every Monday to Friday.

It was about this time that Robin started to show hyperactive disturbance every weekend after his three weekly injection of Depixol, which was usually given on Fridays by the social worker. The disturbance would start on Saturday, going into Sunday and trailing off on Monday. At the next appointment with the consultant I mentioned this, hoping something could be done about it.

When the social worker came to give the next injection in only two weeks, I could hardly believe it. It meant I had to cope with Robin's disturbed state every two weeks instead of three. The social worker said the reason was because the consultant thought his disturbance was due to insufficient Depixol, in other words his disturbance was from mental illness not allergy due to the drug. Knowing of Robin's allergies, I did not believe this. I asked if he could be put on Largactil as this had been used previously, and he had no bad reaction to it. This was granted. Largactil is not a pleasant drug (they give it to pigs), and I hoped that another drug might be found soon and all I had to do was wait.

Worse was to follow. The Newcastle Emlyn Occupational Centre, after several years without concern, now suddenly decided that bringing Robin's own food was psychologically bad for the other clients and Robin should have the same food as them, as provided by the centre. This meant ham, sausages and other processed meat

138

were on the menu, laced with additives harmful to Robin. I can only presume the order came from the consultant as on subsequent visits he made it quite clear he thought Robin's allergies were nonsense and any disturbances were due to his mental illness (which we now know was a misdiagnosis as Robin is autistic). I was devastated, knowing that Robin needed the therapeutic help from Newcastle Emlyn. He loved going there and meeting people.

It was then a church member told me about an allergy clinic in Coleford in the Forest of Dean. It was run by a Dr Hodson, a fully qualified doctor specialising in allergies. I felt I had found salvation for Robin. If I could get it written down by a doctor in the allergy field, surely this would prove once and for all that Robin had allergies, and notice would have to be taken. I decide to write for an appointment forthwith.

The day of the appointment arrived and I drove with Robin the 80 miles to Coleford. We found the clinic, address the Marshes, Coleford, and the brass plate besides the entrance door read:

Doctor A. H. Hodson, MA (Oxon). MRCS, LRCP, FRSM.

It couldn't have been better. Dr Hodson was a fairly tall, slightly greying, very charming man. He complimented me on the way I had established Robin's allergies according to the best-seller by Dr Richard Mackarness, whom he knew about, I told Dr Hodson the disturbance Robin had experienced from the Depixol injection and that at the moment he was on Largactil temporarily. Dr Hodson told me he would write to Robin's consultant and tell him that he could desensitise Robin from Depixol. But Robin's consultant in Glangwili hospital, Carmarthen, never replied to Dr Hodson's letter. Such was the animosity between different factions of medicine in the 1980s. I was devastated. I knew Robin was at serious risk. He would get disruptive and consequently be given more drugs to subdue him. What next?

Chapter 63

More Clouds on the Horizon

So Robin went to the Newcastle Emlyn centre without his own food, with me worrying. The first ominous signs were that Robin started to be disruptive in the ambulance bringing him home, and they requested me to bring him in and collect him, but they also said he should now attend the daily therapeutic psychiatric ward in Glangwili hospital in Carmarthen 30 miles away as there were more trained staff there than in Newcastle Emlyn who would be helpful to Robin. This I did, driving him in daily and collecting him.

A few days into his new therapy unit I went to collect him. Robin wasn't there; he had been taken to St David's mental hospital with a restraining section. He had attacked (so it was said) a member of staff. I was allowed to bring him home after 24 hours, which I did. In his pocket was a discarded empty bag of flavoured crisps – full of additives! I took him the next Monday as usual to the unit but had also written a letter telling the kitchen staff which foods really upset him and were to be avoided, mainly Spam, ham and sausages which contained monosodium glutamate, which sent Robin sky-high, and flavoured crisps. He could have ordinary unflavoured crisps. I felt with this information they might honour my request. Not so. The very day they had my letter requesting not to give him sausages which contained monosodium glutamate he had sausages for his mid-day meal, and when I arrived to collect him, he was being restrained by two male members of staff, one each side, He was taken again to St David's mental hospital under a restricting order.

This time I was not allowed to bring him home the next day. It looked to me as if it could be weeks before they discharged him.

140

They would reassess his medication and change it according to what they thought was his need. I realised that no letter or request of mine would ever be honoured. There was a member of nursing staff (called Charly) who said to me: 'I believe you, Mrs Wood' – a small comfort when the rest of the health team, including the consultant, thought Robin's outbreak and sausages for lunch were only coincidence. I now felt completely alone. If the medical team wouldn't believe me, who would? And what nightmares would the future bring for Robin? Now with Robin hospitalised, I failed to be able to think clearly and felt I wanted to get away from everything to help me reassess the situation.

There was an advertisement in the press for paid volunteers: a firm in Merthyr Tydfil, Simbec, wanted people to help in their drug researches. I, then in my seventies, applied, went there for an interview and agreed to their request. I was to take part in a drug trial which consisted of taking blood samples half-hourly after taking the tablets which were on trial. I never asked what drugs they were. I was to be paid for this service. I considered that if my Robin had to take the drugs as prescribed by the consultant, I could do the same in similar circumstances and I would send some money to the Schizophrenia Association in Bangor, where they were researching into mental illnesses and hoping to find a cure. This seemed to me to be the only way that I might be helpful to Robin, possibly still believing he was mentally ill.

Simbec were very kind and even paid for the dog to go into a kennel. I was to sleep in their little hospital ward, which now has grown into a large hospital to accommodate more people. While there, I explored Merthyr in my free time and found it to be a very nice town, especially the surroundings. The drive to Brecon seemed fantastic to me and the Brecon Beacons reminded me of Switzerland. I was in a ward with several other women and made friends with only one that I later visited. The people in charge seemed to notice the unfriendly atmosphere and gave me a room of my own, which I appreciated. When the drug trial was over I returned home and sent some money to the schizophrenic society in Bangor, feeling I had done my little bit and now would be able to look at my other problems in a new light.

Chapter 64

The Accusation

When back home, on my first visit, Robin, in his slow way, told me that a man had come into his room and showed him his 'willy' and asked him to touch it. Robin looking at me with eyes saying what are you going to do about it. I complained to the nursing staff, who said they would look into it. It emerged, or so they said, that the man had now left the hospital and that Robin would be moved nearer to the nurses' room (so they must have known this man's questionable behaviour, so why have him next to Robin's room?). With Robin's confusion I felt no harm had been done; anyway, he has his own way of knowing where he stands. When we were on our visit in Switzerland at my nephew's house, his wife Gerda, a well-endowed, kindly woman, used to give Robin a bosomy hug. I said to my nephew, 'Go on, give him a hug as well', which he tried to do. But Robin pushed him off, saying, 'Get off', which amused us all, so showing he had no inclination in that direction.

I went home and thought no more about that incident at St David's hospital. But from that moment it seemed as though Pandora's box was opened. First I received a letter telling me two members of staff would visit me at my cottage to discuss Robin's therapy plan, and it gave the day and the time. I made sure the cottage was in perfect order, baked some little cakes and got the best china ready. The two staff nurses duly came as promised. After some pleasant conversation about the weather etc. the tone suddenly changed. I can only say the insinuation quite plainly wrapped up in ordinary conversation was that I had abused Robin sexually and he had confirmed it (saying 'Mother did') when questioned. Robin no way calls me mother, only mum. I cannot

142

remember how we parted or in what manner they left. I was stunned and must have sat still for about an hour with tea cups and left-over little cakes staring at me.

How could they question my poor disturbed confused Robin? He would say yes to anything if he thought that was the reply they wanted. I also felt my cottage had been violated with muck. If two members of the health team believed what they alleged, how many other members of the team in Glangwili hospital believed these outrageous allegations? What about the man in charge, the consultant? Did he know and support these allegations? I felt suddenly alone, vulnerable and degraded. And what about poor Robin having to go through questionings he would not quite understand? And I, having to fight something in my seventies which would have been one of the most degrading things to be done to a son?

I awoke from my shocked state and phoned my daughter in Ross-on-Wye. Her reaction was: 'Stay where you are. I'll come over, and you're coming home with me. We shall visit my solicitor in the morning.'

Chapter 65

Pandora's Box

My daughter Jennifer's solicitor wrote to the consultant in charge of the Carmarthen psychiatric unit at Glangwili hospital straight away. Now Pandora's box really spilled out. Robin's alleged misbehaviour came to the fore as an excuse for the allegations directed against me on that fateful meeting at my cottage with two members of the health team.

This is part of a lengthy letter sent to us in response from The Mental Health Unit, St David's hospital, the mental hospital for Carmarthen and the hospital which takes patients from Glangwili psychiatric unit, which was kept in my Robin file:

> On 3rd June 1991, a meeting was arranged between a number of key staff who would be caring for Robin in the Rehabilitation Unit to review Robin's progress and to formulate a detailed Care Plan for his future care. I understand that you were invited to the meeting, but that you were unable to attend. [This is untrue I was not invited. I would gladly travel the 30 miles to Carmarthen for Robin's sake, where I visited almost daily.] It is clear, from looking at Robin's Care Plan that his inappropriate sexual approaches to members of staff were a matter of considerable concern and were one of three major areas in his Care Plan which were addressed.

Shock and horror, this was the first I heard of Robin's alleged sexual misdemeanours.

This letter from my daughter in response to a visit by Mr Davies from the St David's hospital, after the allegations (17th August 1991), gives the best view of what happened and why:

144

Dear Mr Davies,

Thank you very much for visiting my mother and myself on Friday 16th August, but there is one matter which is troubling me.

Our discussion included reference to point 2 of my letter dated August 2nd and it was suggested Robin 'had touched or groped' female members of staff. Robin had never behaved in this way at home. He has attended the Gateway Club for many years, Church and Church social functions, Cardigan Badminton Club, family gatherings, holidays, dances; the list is endless and there have never been any problems of this kind either with other people or with his own sisters, nieces, friends, etc.

If any touching took place it was probably out of curiosity and without sexual motivation, and I am sure the staff who are responsible for his daily care, Peter his social worker, his GP and everybody who knows Robin would confirm this.

There is a great danger of this matter being exaggerated to justify certain recent actions, and if not resolved now, their implications could have awful repercussions for any future plans which are made on behalf of Robin.

Have you met Robin? I wish now we had shown you our holiday videos. Robin is extremely receptive to suggestions in an uninvolved way, and exhibits a delightful naivety. His understanding of such matters, apart from his own physical frustrations, would be innocent in the extreme, and the result of watching others. If you have not met Robin I would urge you to do so. Robin is imitative in his behaviour and speech, recalling and repeating details of trivial conversations which took place years ago. Although he does not like to do something he does not want to, anything new has to be directed and supervised. He does not have the imagination, for want of a better word, to follow through an original line of thought and actions. His communication with others is limited.

This leads me to my second concern already mentioned in point 4 of my letter. The actions taken by certain members of staff may have created a 'problem' that did not exist except in the minds of those who questioned him. The clumsy attempts that were made to 'encourage' Robin to talk about such matters

145

would have exaggerated incidents that probably had a simple explanation. Robin is a simple lad, and may have observed others in the hospital or even on television. Robin can be happy and enjoying himself, but he has no understanding of being teased, jokes, or playful behaviour. Maybe another patient had at some time said 'touch the nurse'. Or could it have been Robin's first muddled attempt to communicate with a member of the opposite sex? If so it would have been a great breakthrough if handled sensitively by a trained professional psychologist.

Please do not allow Robin to be labelled as having sexual problems of an anti-social nature. He has enough problems without new ones being created for the convenience of others.

Second letter from my daughter to a Mr Jones (also involved in the matter), 2nd August 1991:

Dear Mr Jones,

There are a number of points in your letter dated 30th July 1991 which need clarification.

1. My mother was not invited to the meeting on the 3rd of June 1991 and was told 'not to bother to attend' and didn't realise that anything of importance regarding Robin was on the agenda. Robin did not return that weekend.

2. The information that Robin was making 'inappropriate sexual approaches' to members of staff, including asking them to 'touch my willy', particularly towards older members of staff, would have been a matter of considerable concern to all of us, if we had been told what was happening, and no doubt we would have pointed out that this behaviour began after his admission to Tyler Ward. Staff Nurse Wootton referred only to his asking 'to be tucked in'. [A thing he did at home; I always tucked him in and saw no bad innuendo in doing so.] It again illustrates his childish needs.

This letter not only gives an accurate account of Robin, but points towards what we now know: his being autistic not schizophrenic. Jennifer pinpointed what the learned profession failed to see. It also shows a manageable Robin being cared for at home. I drove

146

A disabled pensioner, Robin and myself with Barry Cooper at his strawberry party.
Barry was the manager of R.S.V.P. (Retired senior volunteer programme), for which I
was the local organiser for Merthyr.

Robin on an outing with
disabled.

The coracle man.

Angie (Cystic Fibrosis)

Felix the cat.

Jumbo Ambulance in front of hotel, Lofer, Austria.

Carolyn Howels
voluntary organiser
for Jumbo
Ambulance.

The Pope meeting
Jumbo Ambulance
disabled in Rome.

All disabled who were taken abroad by Jumbo Ambulance. The X indicates Carolyn Howels.

Dr. David Bellamy arrives in helicopter.

Robin, myself and Sue my neighbour with little Edward watching the helicopter landing.

Outing on Cyprus holiday 2001, Robin sitting next to pretty girl.

Social evening.

Swimming pool.

Robin in swimming pool.

Robin socialising with stranger.

Robin by swimming pool.

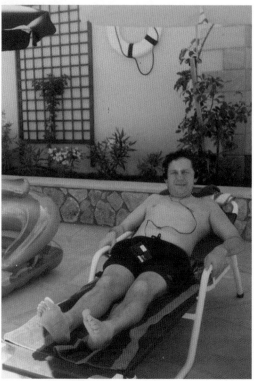

with him to Switzerland, flew to Spain and Majorca. In Cardigan he played badminton every Thursday with the locals, swam once weekly, went with the arts club on outings and rode with the disabled. Yet never did any problems occur and everybody liked him. Then all of a sudden, in only a few months, he was made out to be a sex pervert etc. My 20 years of good care at home and the request for an additive-free diet were ignored.

Money was mentioned at one of the meetings. All we wanted was a written apology, which we eventually got wrapped in a whole page of jargon; I only give the paragraph of the actual asked for apology:

At the meeting on the 16th August, Mr Williams apologised to you that the matter, about which you have complained was raised. I now wish to confirm the verbal apology given to you and to also reassure with you that matters of this nature will not again be raised with you. Clearly the distress you and your family have suffered as a consequence is much regretted. I hope you will accept my apology. If you wish to discuss any matters arising from my response, please let me know.

Yours sincerely,

C. Jones (Unit General Manager).

With regards the man who exposed himself to Robin (and asked Robin to touch him), were the health team aware of his problem and indeed was he admitted because of it? How was he allowed to frequent Robin's room, as stated in a letter in my Robin file, as thick as a book?

Chapter 66

The Decision

I sat in my dream cottage alone, the dream broken, with Robin in St David's hospital, Carmarthen, under a restrictive order. I had in my hand the long-awaited, written apology. Into mind also came one of the first letters Jennifer had sent to Chris Jones at St David's hospital;

Dear Mr Jones,

Following a visit by two of your staff to my mother's home on Tuesday 4th June 1990, my mother and I spoke with Staff Nurse Sally Wootton when we took Robin back to Aaron Ward on Sunday 7th June after weekend leave. She confirmed that to her knowledge Robin had not said what was alleged. We have taken legal advice from Mr David Barry, our solicitor of 44 High Street, Ross-on-Wye, Herefordshire.

Can you confirm with what authority Jane Light and Mark Carole made this extremely serious allegation, and on what date this allegation was recorded in Robin's records? Can you confirm at what staff meeting this allegation was discussed, and can you explain how the 'jump' was made from Robin's alleged asking people at the hospital to touch his 'willy' to allegations of abuse, and can you confirm whether an inquiry into 'a man' entering Robin's bedroom and exposing himself ascertained whether this was a patient or member of staff? Can you confirm what these two people visiting my mother were trying to achieve by causing unimaginable distress to a mother in her seventies who has spent her life caring for her son? We are anxious that this matter is resolved as soon as possible, and that all concerned admit these accusations were made without any foundation whatsoever, and that my mother receives a full apology, and assurance from the medical team that they value the care and support she has always given, and will continue to give Robin. I hope this matter can be expedited within two weeks and look forward to hearing from you.

In reply to this letter came the explanation of all Robin's alleged misdemeanours. Apart from Robin's alleged sexual approaches, I was also blamed for withholding his medication or giving him less. Robin had been home on weekend leave with Largactil syrup. A member of staff alleged there was more liquid left in the bottle on return than should have been. I told the consultant that I would never take off, withhold or alter medication prescribed without good reason. I also added that I thought to send out a potent anti-psychotic drug like Largactil on a home visit in liquid form was extremely inefficient for administering the correct dosage. Later Robin was put on Largactil tablets; but another allegation of withholding part medication was made, when in fact not enough tablets had been sent home with him. When phoning the ward about it, I was told quite sharply. 'Bring him back.' That would have been distressing for Robin and a 30-mile drive for me each way. Luckily my chemist was of a more sympathetic disposition and came to the rescue.

On recalling all these allegations and letters I began to try and establish my next association with the staff who were supposed to care for Robin, and I came to the conclusion that I would never again feel comfortable with them, knowing that they at one time thought me capable of this nasty allegation. I now knew the only thing to do was to sell the cottage and move away from Dyfed.

All this happened because my request for an additive-free diet was ignored and made out to be laughable.

Chapter 67

Good Bye to Cardigan Bay: Fresh Fields, Or So We Thought

I put the cottage on the market and had a buyer in a very short time, so while the sale was being negotiated I went house hunting. I remembered Merthyr Tydfil from my time at Simbec. It seemed a very nice place with the Brecon Beacons nearby and three lovely reservoirs on the way to Brecon, the little Welsh market town which even had a cathedral.

I went to an estate agent in Merthyr Tydfil and he took me to Castle Park, a housing estate three miles out of the main town, fairly high up, near the top of a hill. Sheep were grazing at the back of the house he showed me and I thought it to be perfect for my two cats and Prince the dog. There were walks where you could take your pets. The house was an end-of-link house, with three bedrooms, gas central heating, little lawns front, side and back and a brick garage. From the front bedroom you saw Merthyr town below you, stretching for what seemed miles around, which we later found at night was all lit up like fairy lights. This house was perfect for me, and easy to maintain. It belonged to a young doctor and had been empty for three months, and they were anxious to sell. Inside, it was in very good condition and needed no redecoration. I paid a deposit straight away.

We moved into our new place in March 1991. The day before the move I collected Robin, who was still in St David's hospital, and I wondered whether the people involved in the insensitive, untrue accusation realised why I was forced to move from my beloved cottage. I thought that people dealing with the mind would be able to know what sort of accusations were wrong and what could hurt and upset, and that they could read a person's character

150

(my own) when having dealt with them for a considerable time. How wrong I was. Apparently the consultant, when asked about the incident, said he did distance himself from these allegations. In other words he did not know what his staff were doing. As Jennifer pointed out, matters of this importance should have been discussed at a meeting with the consultant in charge.

The day we moved was a lovely day and everything went as planned. The town hall, the social services, the fire station, the main bus station and the college were all almost next to each other. And there were plenty of shops for all your needs. So the first thing to do was to get Robin into the local occupational centre. At social services I got my first shock. When giving my name they seemed to know more about me than even I did. They certainly knew my name and all about Robin. When I asked for the address of the doctor nearest to my new home, they told me and I went there straight away. When I got there they already knew that I was coming and said in a most unfriendly manner, 'We're full up. Go to the Hollies – they'll take anyone there.' I thought this unkind to the Hollies centre, as we stayed with this surgery for three years and only left because Professor Jonathan Richards opened his new surgery in Dowlais and I knew him as he was a member of the church Robin and I were attending. To get Robin into the occupational centre took over six weeks, which I could not understand, and once again I seemed to have problems with regards to his diet. I thought we were in 'fresh fields'. Wrong again, as we were to find out by and by.

Chapter 68

Robin Goes into a Home, and the 'TENOVUS' Experience

I was advised to let Robin go into a nursing home. 'We have a very nice private home in Abergavenny,' advised the psychiatric consultant of St Tydfil's hospital, Merthyr Tydfil. I was now 75 years old and beginning to worry about Robin's future should anything happen to me. But before entering the home he needed to be reassessed regarding medication. So he went into one of St Tydfil's psychiatric hospital wards. I knew this would take several weeks and asked would they kindly adhere to an additive-free diet. This was granted at first, but did not last very long. I found the attitude of staff changed. I felt they thought I was imagining Robin's allergies. I was devastated, knowing Robin would became hyperactive again and the staff would then blame mental illness and not the diet. So in desperation I tried to find another allergy clinic which might help by putting in writing Robin's bad reaction to additives. A friend of mine told me that St Mary's hospital in London run an allergy clinic.

I wrote on 17th August requesting an appointment. They replied on 24th August requesting a GP's letter. I requested a letter from the consultant, I received an undated note 'to whom it may concern':

Robin Wood, 71 Harlech Drive, Castle Park, Merthyr Tydfil, Mid-Glamorgan

Mr Robin Wood was a patient of mine in St Tydfil's hospital from 2nd March to 24th August, the diagnosis made was schizophrenia. For further details of his illness find enclosed his discharge summary. His mother has written to me saying

152

she is going to take him to St Mary's hospital to have him tested for allergies as she firmly believes that Robin's condition is due to allergy. She also requests an introduction letter and in my opinion a copy discharge letter will be sufficient.

No way would I have got an appointment on that letter and I phoned Robin's social worker, Colin Merrit, in distress and he went immediately to see the consultant himself the same day and returned with a second letter, which I sent off straight away. I received an appointment for St Mary's allergy clinic for 5th November at 3 p.m. Robin was now in the home in Abergavenny. I collected him from there and took him by train to London. Surprisingly we were at the clinic for only a very short time. No tests were made but I was given a chart of additives to avoid, which I duly handed to the home, hoping they would adhere to it with regard to Robin's diet.

I had now joined 'TENOVUS' charity (Ten of Us, started by ten men) for cancer research and sold lottery tickets on their behalf, sitting inside a locked booth with an open window in Asda superstore, Dowlais.

The booth was opposite the sweet stall and I had a full view of the goings-on. To my surprise, when the sweet stall was unattended, children often pocketed sweets without paying. In fact they would stand nearby, waiting till the attendant left for a short moment. Even worse, a dad holding a boy by the hand watched as his boy filled his pocket with sweets then walked away with him. I could not leave the booth unattended as there was money stored from the sale of tickets, so I could do nothing about it except tell the store detective later. He did not seem to be worried, as he said, 'We can't do much about children.'

Many times I saw men being chased by store detectives and brought back into a room behind me, with police coming later and taking the offender into custody. In one incident, a man who had taken two bottles of whisky was being chased and before being caught handed the bottles to an accomplice just outside the door who hid them under a car. The detectives not only caught the man but his accomplice, and retrieved the whisky. Both men were detained till the police arrived and took them away. This created a small crowd watching the goings-on.

Apart from the shoplifters, I could watch people coming and going, and the ones buying tickets often stayed to chat, telling me of friends or relations who had suffered from cancer and they were contributing in the hope a cure would be found, and praising TENOVUS for their efforts. These chats made time go quickly. One of the sales staff often brought me a cup of coffee or tea to keep me happy.

I stayed with TENOVUS for only six months as I felt I needed something more in the line of voluntary work.

Chapter 69

Battered Wives

The voluntary work I now took up for the next four years was joining the Merthyr team 'Tarian' caring for battered wives. This was an eye-opener to the cruelty of men who beat up the woman they claimed they were originally in love with, whose love turned to possessive aggression. A safe house with a secret address was available to take in battered wives and their children, away from the trauma of domestic violence.

No one can imagine the stress of walking away from a home which took years to build up. And no one can imagine what it must be like to leave a man you fell in love with and whose children you had borne. And even after you left you still wonder in your bruised mind: 'Have I done the right thing? Was it my fault? Where have I gone wrong? What is going to happen now to me and my children?' Then the worry, 'Will he find us and what then? Although battered wives are sheltered in a different county from where the battering occurred, some husbands still find them if they try hard enough. (In North Wales at my time with Tarian a man found his wife in the sheltered accommodation and killed her.)

I enjoyed my time with Tarian, taking wives shopping and children for picnics in the Cyfarthfa Castle grounds. It was good to see these children now carefree, enjoying themselves without fear. It was good to see the women who had arrived tired, careworn and having neglected their looks, now slowly starting to care about themselves, gaining confidence and beginning to live again in this new friendly environment.

Tarian would find them a house or flat to start again, to live a normal life. The children would be introduced to new schools and hopefully all would be well. Unfortunately some (only a few) would go back to their offending man, who'd promised to alter his ways, and the whole process would start again. The victims were the children being shunted back and forth. One childless woman was helped by the WRVS to furnish the flat we found her. Two months later she had her offending man living with her. He had moved in with all his belongings. All we could do was watch and hope for the best.

Chapter 70

All That Shines is Not Gold

Problems at the nursing home. Robin had now been at Ty Gwyn for 18 months. I was not happy with his progress, or lack of it. Here is a copy of the letter of complaint my daughter sent on my behalf on 4th February 1994:

Dear Sir,

My brother Robin Wood is at present living at Ty Gwyn Hall, Rosenberg Group of Nursing Homes, Abergavenny, Gwent. I am uncertain whether it is Merthyr Tydfil or Cwmbran who are actually purchasing the services provided for Robin.

My mother lives at 71 Harlech Drive, Castle Park, Merthyr Tydfil, Mid Glamorgan, Wales CF48 1JU. Robin lived with my mother prior to entering residential care at Ty Gwyn. Robin is 38 years old and diagnosed as mentally ill; (we now know different, he is autistic).

I am Robin's sister and I am most unhappy with certain aspects of Robin's care. My mother is worried that inquiries I made may not be helpful to Robin, and it has been inferred Robin could be moved to an even worse place. She agreed Robin could go to Ty Gwyn only because of a similar suggestion by hospital staff that Robin would have to go to — otherwise...

When Robin entered Ty Gwyn my mother was assured he would have a programme of activities and he would be 'rehabilitated', with an aim to make him more self sufficient. No attempt has been made to comply with these assurances. On behalf of Robin I would like the following points investigated and any questions answered.

MEDICATION

Robin has been at Ty Gwyn for 18 months, during this time he has been given a cocktail of 5 different medications at the same time and this included a double dose of Temazepam sleeping tablets. Advice from a pharmacist friend resulted in a strong complaint and his medication has been reduced but concern remains as to why the Temazepam was prescribed and by whom. It is a drug that should not be prescribed for more than a few days and certainly not for 18 months, and not with drugs that act on the central nervous system. The effects are nil after a few days but addiction remains. Why was Robin prescribed Temazepam? Does Robin have a claim for medical negligence?

FIRE RISK

Robin has been given a room on the third floor of a very old building. The staff are on the ground floor. Most of the fittings, banisters, ceilings etc. are wooden and many of the other residents smoke. We understand that regulations state people such as Robin who need help should not be in such a room. If there is a fire, Robin would be at great risk. Why is Robin on the third floor?

FINANCIAL ALLOWANCES

When Robin was admitted to Ty Gwyn my mother asked Social Services for financial assistance since she is a pensioner. Robin spent weekends with my mother and this involved driving 30 miles to collect him and return back. Social services told her to ask at the home for a slip of paper to provide written proof. The Ty Gwyn Patient Services Manager refused to supply this proof and added that they could not keep a bed empty for Robin if she persisted with her request. Another resident says they get £5 'pocket money'. Robin does not smoke, drink or eat sweets, so where does it go? In 18 months Robin has not to our knowledge had clothes bought for him by Ty Gwyn, and we, the family, have had to provide them. My mother has been asked to purchase underwear and trousers. My mother had to ask for a contribution for the six days

158

Robin visited over Christmas (1993) and was given £5 by Ty Gwyn. A gift of £5 from his father was not in evidence and was produced by the home only after my mother asked for it. Robin had no money even to buy Christmas presents for the family... What allowances is Robin entitled to? What are Robin's rights, and what aid is available for my mother?

THEFT AND LOSS

Since Robin has been at Ty Gwyn he has 'lost' a new radio which was a birthday present, a watch, two pairs of expensive Marks and Spencer trousers, underwear, and socks. The final straw is that an expensive jacket bought for Robin as a birthday present on 4th January had been 'stolen' by the time my mother visited the following weekend. The trousers were £29.99 each and the jacket was £35. The total is in excess of £150. Is it acceptable that mentally ill (although we now know Robin is autistic) residents are the victims of continued theft whilst in community care?

CARING

Robin has returned home wearing a shirt without buttons, trousers that were so tight they did not do up properly and hurt his tummy, someone else's shoes that did not fit, and socks with holes in them. At Christmas when we collected him, his underpants were filthy, his shirt buttonless, his socks were not his own and had big holes in them and he was unshaven. He has not seen a dentist for 18 months and no attempt has been made to trim his nails. No one seems to care, yet I understand the care that is purchased for Robin should be of a similar standard to that previously offered by hospitals. Robin's electrical shaver was ruined through no member of staff preventing him trying to shave using the only socket available, just above the bedroom skirting board (floor level). What is the policy regarding care, and also damage to the possessions of the resident?

OCCUPATIONAL THERAPY

Robin is often in bed when unexpected visits are made. Two very small overheated Portakabins are reached via the garden, and the table tennis table allowed no room to move round it. Facilities are dreadful, and Robin does not appear to have an activity or rehabilitation programme as was promised when he first went there. After complaints Ty Gwyn said Robin could do some gardening. My mother was asked to purchase boots and they have never been worn (for gardening) although this was six months ago. The staff moved the exercise bike we bought Robin into the Portakabin, and next to it is the cleaning woman's exercise bike. Are these the facilities!

Ty Gwyn have a mini bus and we were told they take the residents out. We discovered they do a round trip and no one is allowed to get out of the bus until they return home! Rehabilitation has yet to start.

Letters from us crossed with Ty Gwyn's responses to the complaints, some ludicrous, some with little foundation, too many, and much too boring to reproduce.

A case conference followed in June 1994, from which it emerged that his present medication was three major drugs used in mental illness; Loxapin, Procyclidine and Largactil, plus as required (P.R.H.) Flupenthixol and Droperidol. (Five major drugs! Temazepam was not mentioned but always on his medication sheet when he came home for weekends.) He had last been seen by the consultant over six months ago previously.

Another case conference for Robin was held on 30th June 1994. Amongst other 'alleged' bad behaviour from Robin, there followed an allegation which was almost unbelievable. Had I heard correctly? (But it was written down in black and white.) Mr Dave Lewis said that on more than one occasion Robin had said that if he was naughty, 'Mommy hit him with a broom', and the consultant confirmed that Robin had also said this to him, but he was unable to say when he had said it. Robin would never use the word 'naughty' as it was never used at home, and he never called me 'mommy', he called me 'mum' from the day he could speak. Needless to say, Carmarthen health staff with 'mother did' in their appalling, untrue allegation, for which they later apologised, also had made it up. As for hitting him with a broom, this is laughable. Couldn't they find a better, believable one? Dave Lewis also replied that Robin's illness was progressive... This would be proved wrong when Robin joined the home for autistic people.

160

I now came to the conclusion that the bush telegraph used within most authorities and authority to authority to help give the best service possible to new clients moving in, had in my instance been used as a revenge for trouble caused in Carmarthen. They were not able to let me go and start afresh, they had to, so I presume, drop a little hint on the telephone about this troublesome woman deluded into thinking Robin was allergic, and it now gave them delight to stain her reputation. What else could I think?

My own observations in the Abergavenny saga:

1. Robin went in weighing 10 stone. In 18 months this escalated to 14 stone. (I claimed that this was due to too much bread, cakes etc. I thought Robin to be wheat sensitive, or maybe gluten sensitive, which was laughed out of court at meetings.)
2. His promised additive-free diet was not adhered to, in fact at one of the reported meetings it was denied even having been given.
3. To hide his disturbances due to additives, he was given multiple medications by the consultant.
4. He was not given his entitled pocket money for the 18 months he was there (£390).
5. Staff and consultant got together, supporting each other in allegations made.

Chapter 71

The St Mary's Allergy Clinic Dilemma

Having been to St Mary's allergy clinic and having given the leaflet obtained from the clinic warning which additives were harmful to Ty Gwyn, I had hoped that notice would be taken. Not only did they ignore the clinic's advice but at one of the recorded meetings Mr Dave Lewis confirmed that Robin was not on a special diet and had not been for some time...

The report of the meeting notes that I said I was promised Robin's diet would be 'preservative free', otherwise I would never have let him come. Dave Lewis and Robert Lovis (nursing staff) both stated that they were not aware of any such promise being made. In the same report comes the most astonishing part, read out by Dave Lewis as extracts from Dr Penny Fitzharris's report from St Mary's hospital 1993. I didn't see this report but he said it clearly stated that diet did not affect Robin's mood and behaviour.

I wrote to St Mary's asking why I had not received this report and for an explanation why the additive-free diet for Robin was not being supported. And why was the home given this report, which would upset Robin?

Letters from St Mary's allergy clinic:

22nd April 1999 From The Chief Executive David Highton

Thank you for your letter ... I am very concerned about the events that you have described and can assure you that a full investigation is currently underway. Once this has been completed, I will contact you regarding the outcome. You may expect to receive a reply within 20 working days.

18th May 1999 From Liaison Manager Fiona Smith

Sorry for delay, but our inquiries are taking longer than expected...

9th June 1999

Sorry for delay but enquiries are taking longer than expected...

18th June 1999

Dear Mrs Wood

Thank you for your letter 14th April 1999 outlining your concerns about the care that Robin Wood received in our allergy clinic. I apologise for the delay in responding to your letter, but your complaint has now been investigated and I am now in a position to offer the following comments.

Firstly I have to inform you that Dr Penny Fitzharris left the trust some time ago. I therefore asked our current consultant allergist, Douglas Robinson, to review Robin's notes...

The main concern detailed in your letter is that Dr Penny Fitzharris wrote a report on Robin in which she stated that diet did not affect his mood and behaviour. Having read Robin's notes thoroughly, I can assure you that we have found no evidence of such a statement. Although Dr Fitzharris sent a letter to the consultant at St Tydfil's hospital in Merthyr Tydfil, there is no indication of any such report being sent to the Rosenberg Association... Unfortunately we are unable to provide you with a copy of this report...

With regards to tests carried out at the clinic, they claimed to have done the requested gluten/wheat sensitivity test and found it to be negative! (I know that no tests were carried out. I was with Robin for the very short time of less than half an hour that we were there, and how would St Mary's view the fact that in 2004 in the allergy clinic in Cardiff where Robin was taken by the autistic home he is in now, they found Robin to be gluten/wheat-sensitive positive?)

St Mary's claimed to have sent a report of results of tests carried out to the consultant. I wrote to the consultant requesting to see this report. His reply on 29th September 1999:

Dear Mrs Wood,

Thank you for your letter concerning Robin's test results of investigation done at the Allergy Clinic, St Mary's Hospital 1992.

I am sorry but do not have results of these tests...

Dare I presume that a telephone conversation initiated by the consultant or a member of staff from Ty Gwyn took place, giving an unsympathetic report of myself and Robin even before we arrived at the clinic?

Chapter 72

The Bethlehem Hospital

Opposite King's College hospital in Denmark Hill, London, is The Institute of Psychiatry. In desperation I wrote to them explaining Robin's condition (and what we thought was over-medication). I had a reply forthwith and was given a vacancy at their hospital, The Bethlehem in Beckenham, Kent. I took Robin there on 1st August 1994. I had mentioned Robin's allergies to additives and was told they would honour them. He was in the Bethlehem hospital for three months and they took him off all medication and put him on only one, Lozapine. Due to the great distance (300 miles) I visited Robin only once and found him to be his old sweet muddled self. They had no problems with him, no aggression, and no hyper-activity. The asked for diet had obviously been observed. I brought him home just before Christmas feeling we had at last achieved some success.

During the time Robin was at the Bethlehem hospital, I threw myself into further voluntary work. Barry Cooper, the manager in chief of RSVP (Retired Senior Volunteer Programme) had come from Cardiff to find an RSVP organiser for recruiting volunteers in Merthyr Tydfil. I was still with Tarian (battered wives) and was put forward as a possible candidate. After being interviewed and offered the position, I jumped at the chance. It was something I knew I would enjoy. So during the first year and during Robin's stay at the Bethlehem hospital I managed to recruit 32 volunteers in Merthyr Tydfil. The men I would guide into voluntary drivers' jobs (expenses paid) at Barnardo's, others to driving patients to hospital appointments, taking them back and forth for cancer care etc. The women liked to help with reading in schools for the little ones and immobile volunteers were knitting for the premature baby units at Prince Charles hospital.

165

When I brought Robin home from the Bethlehem hospital, a new home had to be found for him. He went into St Tydfil's hospital while waiting for a vacancy. The staff took the reports from the Bethlehem hospital seriously and kept him off additives, as this was mentioned. So there followed a very happy time for me and Robin as I was able to visit him daily, the hospital being only 5 miles away.

Janet Thomas, a very kind social worker, took me around to different nursing homes in the area. There was one near Gloucester that I was not very impressed with. They had a swimming pool with no water in it and they kept horses which seemed well cared for, while the only resident we saw was wandering aimlessly to and fro. Then we saw another home near Swansea and there was only one resident in a kind of occupational room doing some work. Anyway, Janet thought perhaps Thomas Town House, a Merthyr Tydfil Borough-run rehabilitation unit for people leaving the psychiatric unit, might be suitable for Robin.

So Thomas Town House was chosen and Robin was admitted there. As before at Abergavenny, they were going to give him an additive-free diet. I thought all was going well, but I'm afraid this did not last. Was it again the bush telegraph? Or was it because staff didn't like to do shopping and cook for Robin, as they seemed to prefer to get Chinese takeaways and pizza all laced with additives for the other residents (this seemed to be rehabilitation). When Robin started to be disturbed again there is no doubt they had ignored his diet.

Now followed a time when Robin was made out as not only disturbed and disruptive but even a sex pervert. I know at home he sometimes would call out from the top of the stairs, starkers, 'Where are my pyjamas, mum?' And I would order him to go and cover himself with his dressing gown, which he would do straight away (again, being unaware of this being anti-social was a sign of his autism). I can imagine the young girls employed by Thomas Town House seeing him doing something like this and going into a tizzy.

To cut a long story short, it was deemed Thomas Town House was not suitable for Robin and he could not be rehabilitated there, so a new home had to be found. Once again he had to stay in St Tydfil's hospital for a few weeks and once again he settled down without being disruptive. As his diet was honoured, the staff even

166

asked me which foods were the most disturbing ones, and once again I spent afternoons visiting him and sometimes taking him for a drive.

Chapter 73

Another Nursing Home

The next home was Cwm Celyn, Blaina Gwent. This was a very newly erected two-storey home in excellent order inside and out. My hopes rose high. Again the recommended diet enforced by St Mary's allergy clinic leaflet was honoured. All went well at first, just as before, then the diet problem (or was it another bush telegraph from Carmarthen, Abergavenny or Thomas Town House?) once again came to the fore, rearing its ugly head, and Robin once again started to be disruptive. Or so it was alleged. He was sent back to St Tydfil's hospital for medical re-assessment (more drugs to hide his allergies). There he once again settled down without any disturbances. Due to the bad report from Cwm Celyn his medication once again went up. The good thing was that I could again visit Robin every day and take him for an occasional drive. It took about three months before deciding what to do next.

Then came a most extraordinary meeting between Cwm Celyn nursing home and the hospital staff, myself and Marion, a church elder and church consultant, a friend of mine.

Present were the consultant, sitting next to Karen, the matron of Cwm Celyn, and opposite a senior staff nurse from St Tydfil's hospital psychiatric ward, sitting next to Lyn Roberts, nursing consultant, and me with friend Marion in between.

I'm not going into what was said word for word but it became quite obvious the matron either overstated all incidents or was instructed (by whom?) to pulverise Robin and myself. Strangely none of the incidents alleged were ever reported to me and at what date they happened, this being a usual practice.

The report from matron went something like this:

Karen (the matron):	... and he pulled down the curtains and broke the window...
Hospital senior staff nurse:	We've had no such problems with Robin...
Karen:	He broke a chair and threw it...
Hospital senior staff nurse:	We've had no such problems with Robin...
Karen:	He attacked a member of staff and jumped...
Hospital senior staff nurse:	We've had no such problems with Robin...
Karen (finally):	But we can manage with Robin's problems...

Marion's presence gave me so much courage I became quite bold and put forward that Robin needed more activity; although the home was a very lovely place, activities were nil and Robin seemed to be in bed whenever we called. I said that I knew of a home where activity was foremost (this I learned when invited to the annual party of Advocacy, run by Ann Amos, during my voluntary work). I could see Karen being uncomfortable at this suggestion; surely she didn't expect Robin to come back to the home on this appalling report? Anyway, Lyn Roberts and the hospital senior staff nurse knew nothing of our previous troubles and agreed with me that this was an excellent idea. Getting funding might be a difficult and lengthy process, as Lyn Roberts pointed out; she apparently knew the staff there were much more numerous, almost one to one with the residents. So it was decided to try for this home and that Robin should go back to Cwm Celyn till the funding was through. I was horrified at the prospect of Robin going back there. After the meeting I saw the consultant in the corridor and asked him, considering the unhappy and bad report on Robin at Cwm Celyn, whether could Robin stay at the hospital since he seemed to be all right there. The consultant said: 'The psychiatric ward is for acute patients only. No, Robin has to go back to Cwm Celyn.'

I went back next day to the hospital to visit Robin and found out that he had not been sent back to the nursing home. He was still in the hospital, and the next day ... and the next day ... and the next ... The hospital staff, wonder of wonders, must have come to the conclusion that to keep him there was in his interest. This shows the hospital staff's caring attitude. He remained in his usual ward till his admission to the new home six month later.

Regarding the matron's rhetoric, I was dumbfounded. I thought we had had a good relationship and she failed to mention anything good about Robin, who does not smoke or buy sweets and with his pocket money accumulating, donated £110 to Cwm Celyn to purchase a foldaway table tennis set and a new dart board. Plus, I won a large food hamper with Christmas goodies from a lottery ticket I had bought from the Midland Bank, and guess what did I do with it? I took it to Cwm Celyn.

On hindsight it seems curious that the list of nearly 20 complaints from Cwm Celyn seemed similar to the Abergavenny report at one of their meetings. Could it be collusion again?

And the foldaway table tennis set was given because they had nothing to do in the evenings, which is happening in other homes. I think wherever there are more than four male residents, some sports (table tennis, snooker etc.), should be available.

In the middle of his stay at Cwm Celyn I took my disabled son with his horrific reputation for a holiday. I knew it would be the last one, as I was now in my eighties, so I wanted it to be a holiday to be remembered. I chose Cyprus for two weeks, but that is another chapter.

Chapter 74

The Cyprus Holiday

We went in June. Robin seemed to enjoy the flight to Larnaca airport, which took several hours. This was not his first flight as he had been to Switzerland, Spain and Majorca by air. He was his usual mild, slightly confused self.

In Cyprus we were in one of those holiday villages by the Mediterranean Sea. The two-storey buildings are built around the swimming pools, one for adults and one for children. We luckily were conveniently allocated a ground-floor apartment with its front door facing the pool. We spent the days in and out of the pool, Robin being a good swimmer, and we rested in between on the provided sun loungers, lazing in the glorious sun. In the afternoons I took him to a restaurant that had a dart board as he loved playing darts. In the evenings there were entertainments, but Robin was usually too tired and I would watch TV as the British channels were available.

All meals were in the restaurant, and home cooked. The choices were fabulous and of a good variety. I had no problem with Robin's diet, as there were always plenty of fresh vegetables and fruit available. We went on only one excursion, which was to Egypt by air; we were to visit Cairo. I thought this would be the last time we would have a chance of seeing the wonders of the Pyramids and booked up regardless of the cost (£140 per person). We started off at 6 a.m. and flew to Cairo with a group of other holiday-makers. We were taken on a tour by coach through the city and I was amazed to see high rise tower blocks, or so it appeared, with only square holes as windows. Maybe due to the day and night heat these apartments didn't need glass windows. There were windows in the more select properties but the high-rise tower blocks

171

seemed windowless, brick-built, very ordinary and unsightly with theses holes for ventilation and light. But in contrast the numerous mosques in their splendour outshone any other buildings. We visited the Mohamed Ali Mosque at the citadel and were allowed inside, which was fantastically lit up showing Egypt's architecture. We also visited the museum and the boy pharaoh Tutankhamun all in gold was in major evidence. I had already seen this display in London years ago when it was lent by Egypt for special exhibition. I wondered, did Robin take all this fabulous display in? He seemed to look at it all, following me from one display cabinet to the next.

Then we were taken to the Hilton hotel for a tasty buffet lunch of a delicious variety of exotic foods. Robin loves food and had a great time. Then on we went to Giza and the Pyramids. And there they were in their sandy hot desert, a wondrous sight. Egyptians with their traditional desert headgear, holding their camels, waited for us tourists to buy a ride. So Robin and I had a go together on the same camel and we got a picture to prove it. Unfortunately when the time came to dismount, the camel went down first on his front legs and his head went down low. I fell off over his head, into the arms of the astounded Arab. The camel stood up, turned his head sideways and looked at me with superior nose in the air and blubbering mouth displaying huge long grinning teeth as if to say: 'What are you up to?' Anyway, the Arab gave Robin an Egyptian headdress, and I took a photo of them with Robin's arm around the camel keeper's shoulder with the Pyramids behind them in the hot Egyptian sun.

The last treat was a cruise on the Nile and to Robin's amusement a floor show plus another luscious buffet were provided. So there we sat gliding past buildings, towns and villages on the Nile, eating and enjoying the entertainment.

We got back to the holiday village after ten o'clock. Robin was asleep all the way back and walked from the airport bus with closed eyes. We'd had a fabulous day to remember for the rest of our lives. Two days after we got home, I took Robin back to Cwm Celyn.

Chapter 75

A Professor's View on Allergies

Professor J. Brostoff from The Middlesex Hospital, London, appeared on a programme on TV about hyperactivity in children and food additives. I immediately wrote to him telling him how I had kept a three-month record of Robin's foods and found additives caused him to be disturbed, and while at home had kept him to a strict additive-free diet. I added that I would like further real hospital tests to confirm this, but coming all the way to London was now difficult as I was 83 years old. Did he know of an allergy clinic near Merthyr? I did not mention the difficulties I had experienced with the homes.

This is the reply, dated 22nd August 2000:

Dear Mrs Wood,

Thank you for your letter and you have certainly done a magnificent job in getting your son back to a sense of normality by diet. I am enclosing a publication which is the proceedings of a meeting that I organised entitled 'Food, Brain and Behaviour'. This gives details of what additives and food can do to children and adults, both brain and their body.

I am afraid I do not know any centres near you that are involved in looking at food additives and hyperactivity. The head of the charity 'Allergy Induced Autism' is Rosemary Keswick and her group might be helpful in giving you details of support groups and work that is being done in autism. Her office telephone number is 01733 331771.

I do hope these thoughts are of help.

With kind regards

Yours sincerely

(signed by Professor J. Brostoff),

By now I was in such a state. I felt getting in touch with anybody else meant I had to tell them about three homes all being in unison, plus the consultant, that I was a mother believing in these allergies, when in fact he was a schizophrenic person with schizophrenic outbursts.

I felt there was nothing I could do; I was caught up in something I could not understand. What next? I just could not see any way of getting help. Robin's consultant was not on my side, he was the one who decided Robin's future and I could only stand by helplessly. When the next home vacancy came up, all this would start all over again and poor Robin would be the one to suffer.

I don't think I had felt so low in years and it is a wonder I did not land myself in a psychiatric ward. At this moment in time I met a friend, a nurse. She was in the surgery where I was registered. She saved my sanity. But that is another chapter.

Chapter 76

The Good Samaritan and the Heart Operation

Broken in spirit and downcast I felt I had no option but to give in. With three homes claiming Robin did not react to preservatives, supported by the powerful consultant, I had to accept what was offered my poor Robin, plus enough drugs to hide his disturbances. Then I met Ann Vaughton, a clinical nurse at the Morlais surgery where I was registered. I had consulted Professor Jonathan Richards and told him my worries and I believe he asked Ann, one of his nurses, to help me with a 'woman-to-woman' talk. She invited me to dinner and there I poured out my inner accumulating worries and frustrations. I don't know how she put up with me, but she even invited Robin next time and slowly my self-confidence returned and I was ready to do battle again. This shows there is no better therapy than to talk to a friend to take the burden off your shoulders.

The first thing I did then was retire from RSVP voluntary work which I had done for five years. I wanted to write a biography of my life as a nurse in wartime to prove I had done my bit in the war and earned my stay in this country. How this would help Robin I didn't know but it certainly gave me much pleasure re-living the past, some of which I had recorded before on my grandson's computer. It took a year to write this little booklet of 66 pages and I felt completely and suddenly free of all worries. Another therapy for depression: write your life story.

Then came my unexpected breakdown. First my granddaughter Melissa was to come down from Norfolk for a visit. I thought a roast duck would be fine. I duly bought a duck and phoned my daughter to tell her about it. 'But mum,' she said, 'Melissa is a vegetarian.' So the duck went into my neighbour's freezer to hide

175

it from Melissa. Melissa and her boyfriend Gavin came Saturday night and stayed till Monday.

I decided to have the duck the following Wednesday after they were gone and invited my daughter and son-in-law to come and share it. They stayed the night. Next morning I woke up panting for breath. I thought I would die. Pat and Dennis phoned the doctor and I still can't believe how quickly the paramedics were there in my bedroom, with oxygen mask and chair to carry me down the stairs, still in my night attire, to the waiting ambulance. As it was early in the morning, Pat and Dennis had barely time to dress. I dread to think what would have happened had I been on my own. Thanks to the duck, I had my daughter and son-in-law with me.

I was rushed to Prince Charles hospital on 13th December 2002. After several tests while continually on an oxygen mask I was told I had a faulty heart valve which needed to be replaced by surgery. I was then 85 years old, and there would be a risk due to my age, but without the operation my breathing would deteriorate. I signed for the operation. I now knew how distressing breathing difficulties are. I was transferred to Morriston hospital heart unit in January 2003. My worry was not that I would not come round from the operation, but what would happen to poor Robin, who had only just joined his new home in Neath. I was in hospital over Christmas and also on 4th January, his birthday, and he was in a strange new place. No Christmas or birthday celebrations! None of the family visited him as they were too busy visiting me.

I did have a heart valve replaced, I did come round, I was still alive and felt like a trussed-up chicken, when, lo and behold, the Neath home brought Robin to see me with two members of staff. So there I lay helpless, and there stood my Robin, 5 foot 10 inches tall, clean-shaven, hair cut nicely, dressed in fresh clothes, looking good, and saying in his deep slow voice, 'Hallo mum.' Not 'hallo mother', as Carmarthen had said, not 'mommy', as Abergavenny had alleged, no, just plain, nice 'mum'. How I loved him at that moment and how relieved I was to see him so well and knowing the home cared enough to bring him looking smart and smiling.

Chapter 77

Food Additives (The Hidden Danger)

Additives are as dangerous to your health as smoking, and worse than the pollution of the environment. Books have been written by doctors and bio-chemists. The *Lancet* has duly reported on these findings more than once. But the Government has ignored the warnings. If we but knew, additive-related ill health may be in line even to overtake smoking-related illnesses.

Many additives allowed in Britain are banned in other countries e.g. the USA, Germany, Switzerland etc. Additives are passed in Brussels by lay people who are often advised by doctors employed by the firms which use these additives, so obviously these doctors support the firm that pays their income, claiming that only minute quantities of these poisons are used and therefore are safe for the consumer. What they don't (or don't want to) realise is that with hundreds of firms using food additives, they eventually build up in the human system and sooner or later ill health rears its ugly head, sometimes even causing pre-natal damage. The risk is to babies, children and even adults; signs of illness may come up in later life in those who have eaten additive-laced foods for years.

Additives are poisons added to prolong shelf life and kill invading bugs. Industrial eczema is one of the conditions people employed by these firms can suffer from handling these poisons. So if an additive can induce eczema, what can it do to your poor stomach and digestive system?

The availability now of organic foods is a boon. But beware I've seen some foods labelled organic that are laced with preservatives. Organic bacon and ham have been sold by superstores containing the preservative E 250 (sodium nitrate), listed as point three risk in Felicity Lawrence's book, *Additives: Your Complete Survival*

Guide, written with the help of several doctors trained in dietetics and bio-chemistry.

So what are these additives?

The allergy clinic at St Mary's hospital, London, which investigates hundreds of children's allergies and gives advice, lists 51 additives to avoid, among them the following:

1) Azo dyes and artificial colourings
2) Preservatives – benzoates, sulphites, nitrates, nitrites and propionate
3) Antioxidants – B.H.T.B.H.A. gallates
4) Bleaching agents – potassium bromate
5) Flavour enhancers – monosodium glutamate (MSG) also called 'The Chinese restaurant syndrome'

How do you know which is which? They are all numbered by Brussels to add to your confusion. My advice is to read all labels and avoid all additives.

Here are some samples of additives and their health risk with factor 1–3 according to their severity investigated by myself in 2000. (It is possible some of theses have been changed but most still remain.)

SUNNY DELIGHT advertised as 'Children love it' contained:

a) E 412 guar gum, can cause digestive upsets & bowel disorder (if consumed in quantity) risk factor 1
b) E 450 sodium pyphosphares can upset the digestive system, risk factor 3
c) E 202 potassium sorbate (sweetener) risk factor 2, also risk of liver damage
d) E 637 acesulfame, tooth decay (who cares, we can always add fluoride to the water), also heart disease risk factor 3, and obesity

ROBINSON'S ORANGE DRINK:

a) E 202 potassium sorbate (sweetener) risk factor 2, also liver damage risk factor 2
b) E 223 sodium metasulphate, destroys vitamin B, and cancer risk factor 3

c) E 637 aspartame, tooth decay, heart disease, risk factor 3, and obesity

RIBENA:

a) E 637 acesulfame, risk of tooth decay, and obesity, linked to heart disease, risk factor 3
b) E 212 sodium benzoate, provokes allergies, asthma skin reaction; in large doses, gastric irritation and hyperactivity, risk factor 2
c) E 223 metasulphite destroys vitamin B, cancer risk factor 3, and obesity

PEPSI COLA:

E 338 phosphorus, an irritant in concentration. General warning: too much phosphorus creates an imbalance in the body. It is consumed almost daily by children and young people, and advertised as sporty and glamorous.

NEW BABY RAINBOW 'BIG BABY POP' (in small bottle, with dummy attached):

a) E 270 lactic acid, risk to babies and young children; not to be used for babies under 3 months. 3 risk factor 1
b) E 100 curcumin turmeric, cancer risk factor 3

FLAVOURED CRISPS (not ordinary plain crisps). Young children's favourite. Many additives:

a) E 621 monosodium glutamate, risk to sensitive people, babies and young children, factor 3
b) E 627 sodium guanylate, risk to babies and young children, factor 1
c) E 104 quinoline coal tar dye (yellow) hyperactivity risk factor 3
d) E 450a diphosphate, bowel cancer risk factor 3
e) E 223 sodium metabisulphite, risk to conception and cancer risk, factor 3
f) E 124 cochineal (red colouring) risk to conception? Cancer, hypersensitivity, risk factor 2

OUR GREAT BRITISH SAUSAGE (BANGER) is full of preservatives, including antioxidants and monosodium glutamate E 621, which is a flavour-enhancer in most processed foods. There is a high risk to hypersensitive people, babies and young children.

Abroad, some of the foods like sausages are seal packed and do not contain preservatives and remain germ free till opened. I have also seen beefburgers from abroad seal wrapped in this manner, so preservatives are not necessary.

The question arises: why? How has it been possible for firms to adulterate our food in this manner and nothing has been done about it in spite of books being written and the *Lancet* having reported these dangers again and again?

Chapter 78

Drug Addiction (and its Deadly Consequences)

GLUE SNIFFING:

A little girl (10 years old) is found dead in a derelict outhouse surrounded by glue tubes. Where were her companions? Had they fled in panic when she fell ill? Did they leave her to die, and who were they? She had not been on her own, the evidence was there to be seen. The place was littered with glue remains. Who started them off with this horrific addiction? The parents may well ask themselves, why? Why our child? Had they not noticed a change in their child's mood and behaviour? Yes, they had, but thought it to be a passing phase. Too late, they lost a child. It is not only children who engage in this addiction; only recently a young girl in her late teens was reported to have died of glue sniffing.

The sale of glue has now been restricted to adults, which has hopefully stopped children being able to buy it without their parents' knowledge.

COCAINE:

Bailliere's Nurses' Dictionary 1940: 'a colourless alkaloid obtained from coca leaves, used as a local anaesthetic and in eye surgery and dentistry. Synthetic forms are stovaine, novocain, eucaine, etc. Taken internally, its long continued use causes insomnia, intellectual feebleness, emaciation, and death'.

Chambers Dictionary: 'an alkaloid obtained from coca-leaves or produced synthetically; an addictive narcotic used medicinally as a local anaesthetic (often shortened to **coke**, *drug sl*)'.

181

We know that often cocaine is smoked by students and young people or snorted – we've seen some of the disfigured noses. Some people try it for only short duration then give up but others become addicted and progress to harder drugs such as heroin. There have been confessions from Members of Parliament that they tried cocaine out of curiosity in the past (student days) but gave up when realising the danger, others have not been so fortunate (or should I say so concerned with their own health).

HEROIN:

> *Bailliere's Nurses' Dictionary*: 'a diacetate of morphine used as a sedative in respiratory diseases'.

> *Chambers Dictionary*: 'a derivative of morphine used in medicine, but highly addictive and commonly abused'.

My experience as a nurse, heroin was the pain killer which was used last of all the other pain killers. Its use made bearable some of the most painful conditions. A patient would go into blissful sleep instead of fighting the cruel pain.

Drug addiction is the curse of our time. It not only rears its ugly head in the big countries with large cities, but even in little clean Alpine Switzerland addiction is a problem. In many countries needles are given out freely to drug addicts to minimise cross-infection (Aids etc.). Imagine the distress caused to a family when their son or daughter is an addict. At first they did well at school, then hopes of a good future for them were dashed to smithereens by the emergence of this dreaded curse, addiction, acquired where and from whom?

Other horror stories emerge time and again of addicted mothers passing on the addiction to their babies, and addicted fathers neglecting their families, taking to crime to feed their habit, often landing in prison. Even some deadly stabbings have been blamed on drug addiction. The police seem to be chasing this social curse everlasting. No sooner have they caught and convicted one drug pedlar than the next one appears on the scene.

In Merthyr Tydfil, as reported in the *Merthyr Express*, the police arrested and brought to court not one, not two, but sixteen people, all accused and subsequently convicted of being in possession, or of selling, either cocaine or heroin, five being of one family, the

182

youngest only eleven years old. Apparently a shop in that area was openly selling drugs and some residents were afraid of going near it. One man arrested had been in jail more than once and another lost his partner and two young children in a horrible arson attack. Petrol had been poured through the letter box and set alight. The house was ablaze and in spite of the fire brigade's efforts the family could not be saved, and all three perished in the fire. Was this drug-related? We shall never know. The children were only pre-school children. How could anyone do such a horrendous thing to a young mother and little innocent children?

The only way to stop the curse of drug addiction is to tackle the menace at its source. It would mean world organisations getting together and declaring war on opium growing, except for medical purposes, no longer turning a blind eye to unlicensed poppy fields and providing an alternative living for the growers.

Is this pie in the sky?

Chapter 79

The Verdict

Robin seemed to settle well into the new autistic home in Neath, except that he had unpredictable behaviour and was disturbed when home on visits. I came to the conclusion that his diet was not adhered to. I wondered if the bush telegraph had got through to the home, or was it the consultant's anti-allergy attitude? I got in touch with Robin's key worker and once again explained Robin's diet at home and how it had been effective and stopped his disturbances. He listened to me and said he would investigate and let me know the outcome. When I visited the next Sunday he invited me into the office and told me they had decided to take Robin to Cardiff to an allergy clinic which was apparently well known for its success. And they would have Robin tested and thereafter follow their advice. I sat very quietly; I did not tell them that he had already been to two allergy clinics, one in Coleford, where Robin's consultant ignored their advice regarding diet, and the other at St Mary's hospital, where no tests were made. I felt mentioning this would only confuse the issue and kept 'mum'.

At the next visit, once again I was invited into the office and the then key worker Kevin told me Robin had been to the allergy clinic in Cardiff and the results confirmed everything I had claimed including a test for gluten/wheat sensitivity which proved positive. (Where did that leave St Mary's allegation of their alleged test having been negative? And where did that leave the asked for gluten/wheat test being ridiculed and interpreted as me having asked for a test for coeliac disease?) I just sat there and the heavy burden of not having been believed for 12 years suddenly fell from me and I felt free.

Like they do at football matches when the winning team goes

184

mad and they hug each other, I had a strong urge to hug Kevin but restrained myself and just tapped his knee in pure joy. I think he understood my feelings. So the autistic home in Neath were the first home behaving in a professional manner, not ridiculing a mother's (a trained nurse's) findings, but getting proper professional advice, and so stopping the appalling misery I had suffered on Robin's behalf, not to mention the feeling of being treated like a laughable imbecile.

I followed this up by sending a letter telling them which foods to avoid and which to allow in my experience, and duly received a letter from Anthony Jeffers, the manager of Ty Gwyn House, Longford Court, where Robin resides.

Dear Mrs Wood,

Thank you for your letter regarding Robin's diet. The information that you have provided will be useful; together with the information acquired during his recent allergy test I have instructed all staff to follow this diet strictly, but am aware that mistakes can happen, but we are attempting to be vigilant to ensure that this is kept to a minimum...

I hope that you are satisfied with the actions I have taken and would ask you to bring any concerns that you have with the service we provide Robin to my attention at any time in the future.

Yours sincerely

Anthony Jeffers

I sat with this letter on my lap for a long time, thinking back over the 12 years of battling with people and consultants who wouldn't believe my findings obtained by diligently testing and recording Robin's reaction, disturbing and otherwise, to foods, for three months. At last Robin was safe. And I could relax, no matter what the future would bring, at 87 years old.

Chapter 80

Has Anyone Seen Felix?

They seek him here, they seek him there,
My neighbours seek him everywhere,
This dear Felix who hasn't got a care.

Hush, hush, don't tell, he is in my house and he doesn't even belong to me. He belongs to my neighbours Lisa and Mark Thomas. I've still got the cat flap from my two cats which I sadly lost when they were 18 years old. Felix must have seen it and come in to investigate my house. Finding me all alone, he seems to have decided I need his company more than Lisa and Mark, who have two other cats. He sleeps in my conservatory and eats in my kitchen. He doesn't purr and he won't sit on my lap, but will sit at my feet or somewhere near me. He likes being stroked and made a fuss of. He is waiting for me and greets me after shopping, follows me up and down the stairs on my stair lift, and has pushed the door of the bathroom ajar, peeped in and seen me in the altogether. So when I realised that he liked me I rushed out and bought a fur-lined cat sofa bed for him. It is placed on a wide chair in the conservatory and he knows that is his sleeping quarters. I also installed a heater to keep him warm on cold nights. He has a white chest, white nose and white paws, just like Felix on television. He has a character of his own, a kind of male dignity. I love him to bits and he knows it. He knows when it is time for bed and usually goes on his own accord into the conservatory and settles into his furry little bed and waits for me to come and give him a goodnight cuddle and kiss. But sometimes he stays upstairs on the landing, waiting for me to come up and collect him, and this is the only time he will sit on my lap as I sit on the stair lift and slowly descend, with him looking around as though it was a scenic Alpine railway.

Sometimes he does not come in at night when he is out on the razzle and I keep coming down to check if he is in (like waiting for a naughty teenager). Occasionally he will sit on my other neighbour's shed roof as though all three houses were his territory, and it is no good calling him in, he just looks at you as though to say, 'All in good time, all in good time!'

So, dear Lisa and Mark, when you are searching for Felix, he is lording it in my house.

Chapter 81

Crimes Big and Small

Does petty crime escalate into more serious crime, like drug addiction? It could be a springboard, and it is certain that many a petty thief learns more criminal crafts while in jail.

PETTY CRIME

Once started, it has to be carried on to keep a steady inflow of money (especially for the drug addict) unless the thief has a daily occupation to earning a wage. Petty motoring crimes like speeding, driving without a licence, tax or MOT, is a daily offence and people queue outside the courts to be heard. Some local papers carry lists of 'Who's been in Court'.

BURGLARY

My own experience came in 1952 when we lived in Chigwell in a cul-de-sac. Three other houses in the same road as us were burgled in the night while all the occupants were asleep. The first thing we knew was when we came down in the morning and found the back door wide open. The thieves hadn't even bothered to shut the door behind them in their hurry to get away. All they took from us was a week's house-keeping money from my husband's wallet, left in his jacket hanging over a chair downstairs. The other three houses were not so lucky. They lost jewels and other expensive items. We must have been the last on their list and so they took the easiest, which was the cash in the jacket. I remember the eerie feeling of knowing someone had been in our house while we were peacefully asleep upstairs; the children, however, thought it an adventure. The police investigated and took fingerprints. We never heard about it again and I don't think anyone was ever arrested. The other houses had been broken into, but we had left a small top window open and it seems this is where they got in. So from then on we never left any windows open no matter how small.

GANG CRIMES

The bigger, more serious gang crimes, like bullion robbery or post office and bank raids, go back in history and even find themselves in Hollywood Westerns. Bank managers and their families have been ruthlessly tied up, the keys of the bank forcefully obtained and the bank raided. Imagine the distress of these people at being unsafe even in their own homes, a feeling which will stay with them for the rest of their lives.

CRIMES AGAINST CHILDREN

NEGLECT: Sadly, neglect is still present in our civilised world, but can be found and dealt with in democratic countries.

ABUSE: Physical and sexual abuse is more dangerous as it can be hidden for years and a child is afraid to tell. The longer it lasts, the more damage to the victim. So often it is perpetrated by a family member or near relative, this being the reason it has not been detected. Often it comes to light through a teacher at school who notices the child's unhappy behaviour, and on her investigation the abuser is exposed and apprehended. The damage psychologically to the child may take years of counselling to heal.

But the worst crimes against a child are abduction, kidnap and murder.

ABDUCTION: Time and again children are abducted from their mothers by a father of a different culture. When the marriage has broken down and the father disappears with child back into his country of origin, the mother, however hard she tries to find them, often fails. Sometimes she does find them years later when the child or children are nearly adults and won't remember her. The distress of abduction leaves the mother with a permanent sorrow, always wondering 'Where is my baby now – happy, or unwell, perhaps even ill treated?' She will never know, a nagging constant sorrow in her mind, though the child or children may lead a normal life in their father's country and settle down with their father and new relatives.

ABDUCTION AND MURDER: The most horrific abduction is the one where the child gets murdered. To mind comes the abduction of James Bulger, the little toddler abducted from outside a shop by two young boys and the horrendous information which emerged piece by piece of the unbelievable cruel treatment on a railway line which led to the child's death. The poor parents' nightmare will haunt them for ever.

KIDNAP AND MURDER: These two are the foulest crimes against a child and its parents. A famous case was that of the first-born baby boy of Charles Lindbergh, the young American pilot who was the first man to fly solo across the Atlantic Ocean, in 1927 at age 25 years, and so became the most famous and celebrated man of that time. Two years later he married Anne Morrow, an ambassador's daughter who became his co-pilot on his next flights and only a few years later (1932) his baby son was kidnapped for ransom money. Then the terrifying details of the kidnapping emerged little by little and the realisation came that the poor baby was dead even before the ransom money was paid (over a million pounds in today's money). The child's body was discovered in an isolated spot near the summit of a hill not far from the Lindberghs' home (as stated in the book *Charles Lindbergh* by A. Scott Berg). The kidnapper, Hauptmann, an illegal German immigrant with a criminal record, was subsequently arrested and found guilty of kidnapping and murder and was executed. The trial in 1933 had worldwide interest, and the sympathy for the Lindberghs' sorrow and loss was evident in all the hundreds of letters of condolences they received. Apparently a wooden ladder which had been adapted and used to get to the baby's bedroom was traced back to Hauptmann. The baby had been chloroformed to stop him from crying. But on the descent with the extra weight of the baby, one of the rungs broke and the kidnapper dropped the baby and it was said he could have died then by the fall or just been injured and killed later. The ransom money, which had been marked, was traced back to Hauptmann. He pleaded innocent right up to the day of his execution (in the electric chair).

No one can imagine the distress of the loss of a treasured baby and the horrific way it died. The Lindberghs were famous and had the world at their feet. Nothing, neither being a hero, having wealth or being celebrated, could replace their precious baby. From then on they never left their next children alone; to keep them safe from kidnapping their homes had to be reinforced with security measures beyond belief.

The book also states that Anne Lindbergh wrote later in another book of her deep distress: 'I had to die to be born again', and that Charles Lindbergh never forgot his first little son, to whom he used to call out: 'Hi, Buster!'

Chapter 82

Anorexia and Bulimia Versus Obesity

ANOREXIA

Not known in the 1940s and not listed in the 1940 nursing dictionary.

> *Chambers Dictionary*: '**anorexia nervosa** … a condition characterized by a loss of appetite and aversion to food due to emotional disturbance, normally leading to marked emaciation, etc and sometimes death'.

BULIMIA

> *Chambers Dictionary*: '**bulimia nervosa** … a pathological condition, an eating disorder in which binge eating is followed by depression and guilt, self-induced vomiting and purging etc'.

A patient can have one or the other or both. These conditions do not seem to appear in poor countries or where famine occurs. In some cases, is the media to blame with the constant praising of slim models and film stars? Are our young people brainwashed into thinking thin is glamorous and thin will get you to the top? Or are some sufferers being pressurised into gaining successful school grades etc?

Our own Princess Diana was a sufferer, who with courage and self-discipline overcame her disabling bulimia.

I've seen a young teenager on television suffering from this disease, with her spindly thin arms and legs that were barely able to support her. Only after she was told death was imminent did she accept treatment, and we hope she was on the road to recovery.

Apart from anorexia, bulimia must be one of the most unpleasant

192

illnesses to experience for a family. The vomiting can be so nasty as to make the helper feel sick, and causes them to retch themselves. Hospitalisation for such a patient comes as a relief for the family. In anorexia, there is as a rule no vomiting and the distress to the family is watching helplessly as a beloved child slowly fades away.

OBESITY

There is nothing wrong with being a little cuddly and motherly. It is excessive overweight which causes health problems. Obesity in children is at this moment in time being addressed by the media. A tuck shop was unheard of in most schools years ago, yet today you hardly ever see a child who has not got some kind of pop drink or a packet of crisps in his hand, even when out walking. Even babies are being fed commercial drinks, some of which are laced with additives. Empty crisps packets litter our streets: another sign of our time where food has to be constantly feeding one's ego.

Slimming products are a multi-million-pound business venture, when all you have to do is eat less to lose weight. Of course not all obesity is over-eating, it can be a glandular condition over which the person so afflicted has no control, or the chronic disease elephantiasis.

ELEPHANTIASIS

Bailliere's Nurses' Dictionary: 'a chronic disease of the lymphatics, producing excessive thickening of the skin, and swelling of the parts affected'.

Chambers Dictionary: 'a disease chiefly of tropical climates, consisting of an overgrowth of the skin and connective tissue usually the legs and scrotum'.

When I was a district nurse, we had a woman suffering from this disease. She had been abroad, but once back in Britain the disease emerged, and when we were called to help she was 34 stone in weight and her legs were like tree trunks. She was by now bedridden and it took four nurses to move her when attending to her nursing needs. Many a nurse hurt her back attending this poor women as the helpful lifting gears of today had not yet appeared on the market.

Chapter 83

Robin, Disabled But Not Useless

Even at five years old, in spite of his slowness and sometime confusion, Robin tried hard to please. I remember how proud he felt when he was 10 years old and collected £25 going from door to door doing 'bob a job' for the Scouts (a tremendous amount in 1961).

At 14 he helped with a milk round for about six months. I was told he should not be doing this as it would interfere with his school work, and I stopped it. I have regretted this ever since. The milkman he was with was a very kind man and liked Robin. He was annoyed that Robin wasn't allowed to continue, as Robin did well under his supervision. I even believe he was a kind of father figure to Robin.

When he was 15, in spite of my full-time nursing job, I took an evening job specifically to get Robin working, and so together we were employed folding blankets. Robin did well by my side, which again proves he can function only with support and being initiated. When this little job finished he spent the £25 on a suede coat which he had for years till it fell to bits.

As I have already said, he was always willing to help in the house, mowing the lawn with an electric lawnmower and did it well, and was and is still a fantastic navigator, reading roadsigns and directions.

Lastly, I don't know if this can come under work, but because he liked painting I enrolled him in the arts club in Cardigan, and as I mentioned earlier, Robin sold two of the three paintings he entered in their Christmas exhibition. Robin mixes his colours and they are very arresting. But again, I used to put the easel and oils out for him; he would then sit, after being started off, and paint.

He painted places from memory. I have a very large three-foot-by-three lovely oil painting by him of Prussia Cove, a place in Cornwall where we used to go on holidays, and I have also paintings of our hundred-year-old cottage in the Forest of Dean.

Apart from work, Robin was quite uninhibited. On a holiday at Butlin's he went up on to the stage and sang a song, to everybody's and my delight. So while Robin was with me or in a person-to-person situation, so to speak, he functioned well. This made me worry about the future when I would be gone. Would anyone else do as I had done in caring for Robin? This nightmare remained hidden in my mind and is the thing other parents of disabled children must worry about.

Luckily, Robin is now in a home for autistic people and they know how to cope and encourage their charges, and he has settled down and seems to be happy.

Chapter 84

Shop-a-holics and the Credit Card Craze

How much is that doggy in the window? Woof Woof.
The one with the waggly tail. Woof Woof.
I do like that doggy in the window, Woof Woof
I do hope that doggie's for sale. Woof, woof.

We all like shopping, getting clothes we think will enhance our looks or nice items for our homes. What better than with the easy way of the credit card. I too fell for this ploy. I got three credit cards, all saying I could spend up to £3,000. What wonder, what joy. Three credit cards all at £3,000 that means £9,000 to spend. Live now, pay later was the motto! I needn't wait; I could get anything I wanted straight away, anything at all. The repayments would be easy, only a fraction of the actual debt. It was only after a few months I began to realise, when the statements came back, that I was in fact paying almost more interest on the three credit cards then the actual debt. I was caught in a trap and, horrified, sat down to think what I should do. There are lenders who will lend you the money to clear all debts. But beware, their interest rates are more than your credit cards' (loan sharks). Hidden away at the bottom of the agreement in small letters is the warning 'non-payment may cost you your house'. I asked my bank for a loan to pay off all the debts, and got one spread over 18 months with payments taken out monthly from my current account. I cut up and threw out two of the credit cards, keeping only one for petrol, which I now pay off regularly when the statement arrives. The 18 months of my loan seemed to pass very quickly. Then I was free, and never again bought more than I could afford.

Other people are not as lucky as the bank might not be able to help. The mother with young children who hasn't got a bank account, who wants the little ones dressed as well as other children, or at Christmas time to get presents and other goodies. The wife who uses the credit card for buying attractive clothes unknown to her husband, she puts them in danger of losing their house.

Then there was, as shown in the media, the girl who was an actual shop-a-holic and nearly ruined and bankrupted her own family with her compulsion to shop for things she didn't even need. She even stole money from her own parents to satisfy her shopping craving.

To mind comes Imelda Marcos, the wife of a deposed dictator. She was found to have over 300 pairs of shoes in the abandoned mansion – though don't some of the famous, and royalty, have the same!

Chapter 85

Neighbours from Hell or Heaven

We have heard much about neighbours from hell, the neighbours who make life impossible with their loud noises and blaring music, the neighbours who insult and harass those living on either side, and the elderly man who even got to such a stage of frustration over a lengthy dispute of a fence that he shot his neighbour.

My first encounter with neighbours from hell came in the 1950s when we lived in Chigwell. The neighbour on my left had a dispute with the neighbour on the other side, over the fence being 1 inch in default. The dispute was long and bitter and eventually my neighbour moved. I don't know who won the court case, but the troublesome fence remained where it was for the new owner.

The next case I was involved in myself was with my cottage in the Forest of Dean. The owner of the bungalow next door, which was built years later, claimed the space between my cottage and his home belonged to him. As I stated in my biography *A Simple Woman an Extraordinary Life*, all our neighbours were simple, friendly, forest people, some farmers, some ex-miners. But there was just one neighbour who didn't seem to like us. His name was Mr Merry, but his name really belied his true nature. There was a four foot gap between our ancient lovely cottage and his modern fairly new bungalow. He claimed that the 4-foot gap was all his ground. (He never complained before to the previous owner, who had built an extension scullery and bathroom on that side.) Anyway, he proceeded to build a wall against our cottage with a gap of only 3 inches, completely covering our bathroom window, stealing our light and stopping us from decorating and maintaining that wall. I kindly pointed out to him our dilemma, but to no avail. When I told him I would consult a solicitor, he gave a hollow laugh: 'You wouldn't dare! '

198

I dared, and after a year of wrangling won the case. He was ordered to pull down the wall forthwith and pay costs and £400 in compensation for distress caused. There was a gasp in court from Mr Merry's supportive entourage (parents, in-laws and half the Forest of Dean). I was alone with only the solicitor and disabled Robin.

Not being a vindictive person, in spite of being glad to have won, I felt sorry for him. As I wasn't short of money, I decided I would go and tell him he needn't pay the money and so repair good neighbourly relationships. His wife's parents had the bungalow next to him on the other side and when I went over to tell him, his wife's mother was hanging out of the top window. When she saw me, she hurled the most obscene language and abuse at me. I left hurriedly. Little did she know how much money she had lost her son-in-law, but no doubt she felt very satisfied with her outburst.

I now decided that the built-on scullery and bathroom building's flat roof could do with a proper tiled sloping roof. What better than with Mr Merry's money (to remind him of his misdemeanours)!

This was not the end of the story, as the builder who put the new tiled roof on this part had to put his ladder on the disputed ground. My four-year-old granddaughter stood wide-eyed as dear Mr Merry emerged from his bungalow shouting and bellowing that we were trespassing with the ladder on his land. The man laying the tiles on the roof, a big brawny fellow, shouted down, 'Yeah, do you want me to come down and sort you out?' Mr Merry disappeared like lightning into the safety of his bungalow, not to be seen again that day.

The funny thing about Mr Merry was that everybody in the Forest of Dean was related, yet everybody seemed pleased (secretly) about the outcome of the court case. I think it was because he thought himself a cut above the rest, being an insurance agent, as most people were small-time farmers or ex-miners. In spite of the case I remained friends with the rest of the community. This was the last unhappy encounter I had with a neighbour. Luckily all my neighbours after that were neighbours from heaven.

Here in Merthyr Tydfil I have June, a midwife living on my left, who took me to hospital when I was unwell in 1995, visited me and brought me back when discharged. My neighbours on the right, Lisa and Mark, I thought I had offended over parking and sent them a card explaining with an apology, hoping I was not a neighbour from hell. In return I received a little present and letter:

Many thanks for your card and letter. May we say that you are an excellent neighbour and no trouble at all. Please don't be afraid to ask for anything if you need it (and we mean anything). If you need shopping, putting your bin out, your grass cut, please, please just ask. And you are welcome to call in any time if you fancy a cup of tea or some company.

How's that for neighbours!

Then there's Tony and Karen opposite. Tony will do anything, be it plumbing, electrical or other work. There was the day I left my key indoors and shut the self-locking door behind me. I have a small conservatory at the back which is 8 foot across with a cat flap on one side and a door on the opposite side. The door is shut from the inside with the handle pointing downwards. You lift the handle to the horizontal position and you can open the door inwards or shove it open from outside. So Tony my neighbour came with a 10-foot-long pole (goodness knows where from), got to his hands and knees by the cat flap, shoved the pole through and wiggled the pole to and fro, trying to touch and shift the door handle 8 feet away, with me standing behind him biting my nails. Yes, after trying hard he did manage to hit the handle into upright position and hurray, I could open the door from outside.

Another time I ordered a bed settee which was delivered to us, but the men could not move my sliding door sufficiently to get the old high back settee out. They did not have the knowledge of the removal men who had brought it in. So there they were at my door with a settee waiting to take the place of the old rather larger settee, not knowing what to do. I saw Tony's van and knew he was in so I rushed across. Tony is about 6 foot 3 or 4, a very large man with a very large generous heart. So there was me, a mere 5 foot 2, asking him timidly: 'Can you lend me your chainsaw?' He looked down at me puzzled, no doubt imagining me with a powerful chainsaw vibrating madly in my hand and shaking me back and forth so that I was barely able to stand still. Then he came across himself and sawed the offending settee to bits, put it in my front garden and said, 'Don't worry, I'll take it to the dump.'

My other kind neighbour, Beth Booth, brought me many dinners when I was just out of hospital after my heart operation.

And of course my laptop, which I use only to type and print, is full of unsolved computer mysteries which have been solved time and again by Tony and Steve Booth. What wonderful neighbours!

Chapter 86

Robin's Open Day at Glamorgan House

Glamorgan House is approximately 1 mile from Longford Court, a new attractive three-storey building. It was built with the sole purpose of catering for the psychological needs of autistic people and getting them into a work situation to make them feel useful and part of the community they found themselves in (often a home for autistic people). It is designed to further or bring out hidden skills in art, pottery or any other talents. I went with a friend and we found every room extremely well constructed, with ample space and everything you might need for the particular craft being practised therein.

There is a pleasant canteen for coffee breaks and midday meals, with a training kitchen attached. All staff were so helpful and always smiling, a kind of therapy in itself for disturbed people. I was allowed to see their staff book and found the responsibility of staff towards service users (autistic persons) was emphasised time and again. Here is an excerpt:

> It is vital that staff try to keep service users to their structured timetable. In time this 'new' routine will keep people calm, as 'their' day will be more predictable. Staff must take care not to overload service users, [*sic*] too many demands, too much information, too noisy an environment, poor communication to service users. Any of the above causes (triggers) may be avoided if they are recognised.

My friend and I were impressed and I was very glad that Robin was able to take part in those activities offered.

When I first took Robin to Longford Court and saw some of

the boys there, so very autistic and even disturbed, my heart trembled within me. How Robin would react, as he is (I would say) only 50 per cent autistic? His arithmetic is excellent, his reading is good, though I don't know how much he actually takes in. He plays Scrabble and wins often as his spelling is excellent, in fact better than mine. So how would he feel amongst those others?

He went there in November and in December I was rushed into hospital and had heart surgery. So Robin was in this new home for Christmas and his birthday on 4th January. As I have said in the chapter about my operation, when the staff of Longford Court brought Robin to visit me in hospital, and the way he looked, I stopped worrying.

Now I feel that to be with very autistic people is a challenge and should make Robin realise his own advantages and learn to tolerate other people of perhaps lesser abilities. I was very happy having seen Glamorgan House and all it offered, and am happy to know Robin is where he is now.

Chapter 87

Snowflakes, Christmas and Jingle Bells

I couldn't sleep so I went to the window, and wonder of wonders, in the lamplight of our path at the back of the house, snowflakes drifted down like a star-bedecked veil. The snow seemed to settle on my garden wall and on the lawn, and Christmas was only three days ahead. Could it mean we'd have a white Christmas?

My mind wandered over land and sea, across the Channel, over snowy mountain peaks into Switzerland, my native country. The Christmas celebrations were quite different there years ago to the way celebrations are here in Britain. Presents were given out on Christmas Eve by the Christmas tree, which meant parents could sleep in the next morning without being woken up at five o'clock by excited children wanting to know what was in the stocking at the foot of the bed. I always remember the table holding the Christmas tree had a cloth hanging right down to the floor. Under it was hidden a small wicker basket dolly's pram, my passionate wish come true (I was four at the time). What wonder! What delight! Christmas Day was spent quietly, the children playing with their new toys. The main festivities with goose and all the trimmings were on New Year's Day. These were family days when my dad played the zither, my sisters musical instruments from violin to mandolin and piano and sang, and I just sat and listened.

Yes, we did have sledges drawn by horses, ponies, asses, or whatsoever was available, with jingle bells, sliding through the fairylike white-covered countryside. And I remember the year, over 70 years ago, when the Zurich lake froze so thick people could skate on it and there were even little stalls selling hot sausages, soup and drinks on the ice. For remembrance of this unusual occurrence, every child in Zurich was given a medallion with a dove flying over the icebound lake. I don't know what happened to mine. Some time in the next few years it got lost.

I began to feel quite sad, perhaps even a little homesick (at 87 years old?) How could I? I love the Brecon Beacons (my little Welsh Switzerland) and the fantastic drive from Merthyr to Brecon. Yes, the children did bring their tray sledges and what have you next morning and enjoyed sliding down on the hill behind us. Sadly the snow did not last till Christmas. I had Robin home and we spent a lovely Christmas with friends, and to make it perfect my granddaughter and Gavin drove down from Norfolk and stayed four days, giving us their joy and youthful laughter. One day we spent up at the mountain centre and had dinner there and it was packed with visitors. I just loved all the company around us. So this year is one to be remembered.

New Year I spent with Felix, my lovely feline companion. Come on 2005!

Chapter 88

An Assessment Meeting of Robin's Progress at Longford Court

I looked forward with apprehension to this meeting, having had nothing but unhappy occurrences ascribed to Robin at some of the previous meetings at different homes, as reported in previous chapters.

So now to the assessment meeting at Longford Court on behalf of Robin. Present on one side were the day service manager of Glamorgan House (the new therapy building unit for Longford Court), Stephen Hill, the therapy worker in charge of Robin, two carers from Ty Gwyn Longford Court, where Robin resides, and myself. On the opposite side were the consultant and two social workers from Merthyr Social Services.

Oh, yes, there were incidents recorded on a percentages chart: very high at the beginning but narrowing down to almost nil at the time when Robin's additive problem was brought to their attention. Instead of ridiculing my assertion, they made their own assessment by taking him to an allergy clinic in Cardiff, with results proving all my allegations. This was read out, followed by the activities offered for Robin and his reaction to them. He did computer work, pottery and other activities. His planned working day had a therapeutic effect on him and he was progressing well. This was a very professional, unbiased report.

More time was spent on the positive side and therapy work than misbehaviour, which improved my hope for Robin's future. Some excerpts from the staff handbook: 'Maintain a calm environment, avoid unnecessary conversation, when speaking maintain a calm tone and control the volume of your voice – don't shout. Speak slowly when instructing, use short sentences. When client shows signs of anxiety, do something about it, don't wait for an incident to occur. Support service users who look hot and bothered. Avoid interrupting sessions in progress. Assess the environment before allowing visitors to enter due to noise levels and presence of unfamiliar people.' This is professional caring at its best and should be provided by all care homes.

Back to St Tydfil's hospital. I believe that when Robin had a very serious seizure while there, when he injured himself and looked as though he had been in a war, and it was thought to be an epileptic fit (though after a brain scan proved normal), this was in fact a very severe reaction to have been given something very heavily laden with additives. The nursing staff were equally as upset as I was about this occurrence and they asked me which additives I had found harmful to Robin and I gave them a list (the top being monosodium glutamate, which is in most processed foods, antioxidants and some colourings). By following these restrictions, there were no further incidents. Were the nursing staff beginning to suspect that my allegations might be true? But what did the consultant think?

Chapter 89

Reports Fair or Unfair

Prior to Robin entering Longford Court, I had begun to wonder whether there was something in our medical reports adverse to me and Robin. I asked to see them and after much wrangling got my wish in the presence of a social worker. (What did the powers that be think I was going to do with them?) It was very enlightening. The Bethlehem hospital three-month stay under the care of Professor Murray was not included, except that diet was mentioned as having been followed. It was strange that the homes afterwards did not follow this diet. Or had they not had access to the reports? The most damning report was written by a carer at Thomas Town House, a carer with many fewer qualifications than I have. It was full of nasty insinuating beliefs about Robin's character and the numerous bad things he was alleged to have done, I'm not going into the whys and hows. The best way is to give part of the report that Clare Jones, a consultant clinical psychologist from Bridgend and District NHS Trust Learning Disabilities Directorate, did so accurately on Robin. This professional report was not included in the medical report. Why?

CLARE JONES' REPORT

OBJECTIVES

Knowing how to work with Robin and keep him occupied without crowding him.
Better understanding of Robin and new approaches, and get to know other people involved.

208

To move forward towards day time occupation which will give him a feeling of job satisfaction, e.g. painting with the right materials.

Acceptance of the fact that his progress is patchy.

Work together to help Robin with his frustrations.

Gain better understanding.

Identify positive qualities and find a way of developing potential.

WORDS TO DESCRIBE ROBIN

Good looking, solid contact with mum, confused, anxious, polite, artistic, willing to please, well motivated with encouragement, well mannered, loveable, friendly, youthful, wicked, talented, likes to please, enigmatic, satirist, unique, slightly slow in some areas, willing to be taught, better person to person not team, says what you want to hear, uses other people's scripts, a bit like a computer – in and out, complex, interesting, puzzling, spontaneous, quiet versus talkative, good sense of humour, uninhibited in other ways, affectionate, difficult to understand sometimes, unpredictable sometimes, can be self contradictory

It goes on, why is Robin like this? It gives an action plan which is exactly the recommendations given to staff at Longford Court. The point is, Thomas Town House hadn't a clue how to interpret Clare Jones' report, even less how to implement it. There were many very young girls with minimum qualifications working at Thomas Town House who were wholly unsuited to dealing with disturbed people. As for allowing a carer to write a damning report of a disturbed young man, it seems unbelievable and including it and excluding a professional report by a qualified consultant clinical psychologist, one might ask where was the consultant who allowed this to happen to one of his patients? I tried to get onto the consultant but he said it was nothing to do with him, so next I went to social services to eliminate this humiliating report which would follow Robin for the rest of his life, but to no avail. So what is the purpose of being allowed to read it, when offending half-truths cannot be eliminated?

Chapter 90

The Sunday Run

We have had the school run (too many cars?), we have had the film *Chicken Run* (there are hundreds of those), and for the past three years I have had what I call the Sunday run. I get up at a leisurely rate, go to church and after the service, which usually ends at 12 noon, race back home, grab a snack and run (drive) the 27 miles to Neath to visit Robin, who is always ready waiting for me. This is our weekly treat. Robin and I both look forward to it.

We are allowed a room to ourselves where we play Scrabble. We both cheat like mad by helping each other to increase the final counts, including 'illegally' exchanging a much needed letter occasionally. During play, Robin eats all the 'goodies' I bring: fruit, nuts and biscuits. Tea is usually provided and one of their smiling young people will bring it to us. I usually do the adding up of points scored, but Robin keeps a sharp eye on me and is not afraid to correct me if I'm wrong as his arithmetic is better than mine. We usually get five games into the three to four hours I stay with him.

Sometimes I will take him for a little drive and have tea at Verdi's, a lovely restaurant in Swansea Bay by the sea. We have also gone to the lovely swimming pool in Neath, but the staff like to escort us there in case of problems and they don't always have people available.

I choose Sunday for my weekly visit because Robin and the other residents have a proper working programme during the week, morning and afternoon with a one-hour break for lunch in their canteen, finish at 4 or 5 p.m., and then I go back for the evening meal. Weekends they can do what they like; they are taken out for a ride to a place of interest or just stay in their homes in Longford Court watching television. After my visit, Longford staff usually escort me to my car with Robin trailing behind calling out, repeatedly, 'See you next Sunday,' and unless I also say, 'See you next Sunday,' he won't be satisfied. So that explains my 'Sunday run'.

Chapter 91

A Timid Nature or Shyness

Chambers Dictionary: '**timid** inclined to fear or alarm; lacking courage; fainthearted; shy'.

Being timid or shy can be very disabling and distressing. Yet sometimes feeling so very low may be a springboard to try hard to achieve more than expected by everyone else.

A daughter of a friend of mine was so shy and timid she slipped into depression and needed counselling for over a year. She would not go out with friends, she felt too shy. This was as distressing for her as for her parents, who only wanted her happiness. This happened during her late teens when she should have been enjoying life with her friends, but was almost a recluse, hiding in her home.

To be timid and fainthearted is an open invitation to the bully who draws his strength from having power over someone weaker than himself. It happens in school all the time and often goes on without being recognised, as the victim is too scared to tell. Schools seem to be more aware now and try to stop the bullies. But beware, bullies: fortunes sometimes change. The timid and shy girl or boy may try to compensate for their low status by studying hard to prove themselves, and often succeeds. Imagine, the bully grows up and applies for a job. He sits nervously in a line of applicants waiting for the interview. After a long wait he is called in, and there in front of him is sitting the interviewer – none other than the very boy whose life he had made a misery by his bullying years ago. The interviewer had, through hard study, become a chartered accountant and was now in charge of the firm. The bully is applying for the job of an ordinary clerk, and the bullied one is a chartered accountant and employer.

212

Girls too can feel very miserable about being painfully shy and unable to communicate like their forward peers. Yet in a girl it can be attractive; in the pantomime the Prince falls for simple, sweet Cinderella and the forward, clever sisters lose out and cannot understand how Cinders won the love of the Prince. And again it is depicted so well in the novel *Rebecca* by Daphne du Maurier, where Max de Winter falls in love with a shy, timid 20-year-old girl who is a companion to a rich, spoiled, middle-aged woman who cannot understand why a rich man should want to marry an ordinary girl.

Chapter 92

What is Love?

We may well ask. This deep, wonderful thing striven for from the day you were born can lift you up to heaven's height or plunge you to the deepest depths of despair. Freely given, love is like the sun, making your spirit blossom and enhancing your life. The rejection of it can drive you into depression, despondency, suicide or even murder.

Songs, plays and films have been written about love's deep emotion.

John Lennon: 'All you need is love, love, love, all you need is love...'

Beatle Paul's young voice lingers in my mind: 'Love, love me do.'

Or Nana Mouskouri's sweet vibrating voice: 'Only love ... And, I have a dream...'

In my life I've experienced both suicide and murder. I was only 10 when a niece of mine, at the age of only 18 committed suicide by jumping out of a hotel window down into a ravine and was killed. She had a brilliant future before her working in the Bundestag, in Bern in Switzerland (equivalent of Parliament in Britain), a status occupation.

The man she was betrothed to also worked for the Swiss Government. I never knew why they broke up as no one wanted to talk about this terrible outcome. All I knew was that she had been a lovely, pretty, bubbling young woman who used to tease me and chase me around.

The other horrific experience was when we lived in Chigwell. Opposite where our road led to a main road was a shrubbery. There a man killed his (as he thought) cheating wife with an axe. This frightening experience stayed with me all my life, as it was only a few yards from our home.

The third unhappy memory was of some dear young neighbours we had. We had spent many coffee mornings in each other's houses. They had twin baby daughters. We moved away and lost touch. Some years later, to our shock, we found out from the national newspaper accounts that the mother had had her leg amputated because of cancer being diagnosed in her knee. After that it was reported she became impossible to live with, and during a violent argument her husband killed her. I remembered him well as a tall, young, smiling man enthralled with his little twin babies. Had love died between them and soul-destroying arguments taken over, so passionately angry as to destroy all the understanding they ever had between them, leading to murder? He was jailed, and many years later another report stated he was set free. When this tragic event happened the twins must have been in their teens.

Then there was 'The Unknown de la Seine', the beautiful young girl found drowned in the Seine near Paris. Books were written about her and sculptures made (in the 1940s), all being intrigued why such a lovely girl should have committed suicide (so it was presumed). Was it a broken love affair? I had a book myself with the picture of her lovely youthful sculptured face on front cover.

Next, the lasting love I came across during my district nursing times, the love that weathers every storm. To mind comes the lady bedridden with multiple sclerosis. When she married she had been a lovely, vibrant, young girl; now she was completely dependent on others for her every care. Her husband still loved her, cared for her, protected her, stayed by her. This is enduring real love, the love we promise till death do us part. And this was not the only one of its kind I encountered.

Of course the 'Derby and Joan' lifetime-lasting love relationships occur more often than the unhappy ones.

There is also the man who has his 'little bit on the side' but still cares for his family more than the 'little bit', stays and provides his legal mate and family with their dues (a kind of second-grade love). The wife ignores it for the sake of the children, the family honour and reputation and of course the financial situation. To split a family always has enormous consequences. Or perhaps she is blissfully unaware of her spouse's straying ways.

Another lasting pain is not being loved. Love for a child is a normal expectation and when absent will be remembered right into late adulthood, like the man who told me how even though now in his forties he was still secretly grieving that his father did not love him, and he was a vicar.

Then there was the Duke of Wellington, who met a beautiful 18-year-old girl. But his offer of marriage was refused by her protective brother because at that time he had no money. If she would wait he would come again, he promised. After winning several battles, 12 years later and now famous he returned to honour his offer. When he saw her he remarked to his friend, 'God, hasn't she turned ugly.' He married her just the same; he was an officer and a gentlemen. The marriage was not a success. She was overawed by his fame and success and felt inferior. But there were three sons and only when he was retired and old did he realise what a loyal treasure she had been and a late love blossomed.

And lastly, I believe the most precious, sweet, innocent, so readily love given by a child is the one to be most treasured.

Chapter 93

Unemployment

Sudden, unexpected redundancy when a firm becomes bankrupt or takes work abroad for cheaper labour must surely be a tremendous shock. Could it be due to the Government's thinking the increase in the minimum hourly rate would be beneficial to the worker, when in fact it drove firms abroad? Instead of a higher wage, some workers now find themselves out of a job. The shock not only shakes the worker, but the whole family, whose finances now are slashed. They now find the things accepted as normal, such as a car, telephone and other 'basic' items, have now become luxuries. Often these families get caught into debt, an ever-lasting spiral which has driven some unemployed people into depression, ill health, worry and in some cases even suicide. Some are able to find new jobs, while the not so lucky may have to sell their homes for smaller ones with lesser mortgage commitments. The regular replacement of a new car is certainly out. Living standards have to be drastically cut.

I know of a family break-up due to the man being made redundant, and in many cases where the mother who had stayed home to tend to her little children now has to go to work, the unemployed man takes over the care of the family. Sometimes he does not do as well as the mother in caring for the children and they begin to look neglected, though some men seem to cope well under the circumstances.

A lengthy unemployment and unsuccessfully applying for job after job, time and again, must be very depressing. Waiting daily for the postman and the expected letter with, 'Sorry...' is demoralising. I knew the wonderful feeling of being employed and feeling useful when I got just a little job at 80 years old selling charity lottery tickets for Tenovus, getting just a little over a pound per hour. I felt I was back in the social stream and not yet on the scrapheap. That is how people feel (or should feel) when in a secure job. Later I got into voluntary service, followed by becoming an organiser for RSVP (Retired Senior Volunteer Programme), which was even better, and eventually doing a small column for the local press. So my advice to any unemployed person is to do some voluntary work; it will lift your spirits and might even get you into a job. I also found starting with something quite low and simple will often get you higher on the employment ladder. When I started nursing it was in the sluices doing the most menial job (this was often when girls trying to become nurses gave up) but I stayed and then slowly rose and three years later became a staff nurse. Also never stop training in your spare time, learning new skills which are on offer in every community (evening classes etc.). In some firms it is claimed the tea boy of years ago became the director eventually. So my advice is go for anything, you never know where it may lead.

Chapter 94

Broken Relationships (Marriage etc.)

Broken relationships: I should know, I survived two – or did I? The first was in my childhood, I was only seven years old at the time. Our hotel in a small Alpine resort went bust and my father left with the woman who served in the bakery shop attached to our hotel. Apart from the unhappiness, the shame of it in the 1920s was terrific. I was left with an aunt in Berne while my mother sorted out our new apartment in Zurich. My three other sisters were all away from home, one in college, the other two governesses to the children of rich families. I eventually joined my mother in Zurich and went to school there.

My remembrance to this day remains that it took three years to overcome my sorrow and secret wish that my father would come back and we'd be a family again Having been a latecomer in the family, I remember my father, then in his forties, greying hair, moustache curling upwards at the ends, chasing me upstairs for the fun of it. I dearly wanted us all to be together again as we were at the hotel, where we used to have musical afternoons with my father playing the zither and my sisters' other instruments. On cleaning days I remember again my mother sitting on a chair on top of the table so the cleaner could sweep underneath and she sang songs to me while darning. I never got over this family break-up and even now in my old age I'm moved to tears of what might have been.

My second broken relationship was my own marriage when my husband, a wandering type anyway, left me to care for four children, the youngest only five years old. Once again I fretted for three years hoping he would return to me and his four children. But he did not, he had three more relationships, none of them permanent,

219

and eventually married again late in his life (by now knowing his mind). I really did love him and I thought at the time that he was the spitting image of the film star James Mason. We are still friends and in contact. I never married again nor had another relationship; I was too busy caring for the growing family and felt instinctively that another relationship with a man would upset the boys. Besides, I was doing a full-time nursing job to keep the home fires burning and pay the mortgage. Sometimes it felt as though I was swimming against the current all the time.

Today broken families are the norm, it seems. It is the children who suffer; their loyalties are broken. Like me, they must have loved both parents, and awkward situations arise from having to take sides against someone you love and stick to just the one who is going to care for you. Arranged visits may help a little, provided the parents don't talk against their absent partner, which mixes the child up even more.

Chapter 95

Homelessness

After nature's disasters, such as floods, earthquakes, extensive fires consuming whole forests and threatening villages and towns (as in Australia), tornadoes and erupting volcanoes, we watch horrified and helplessly as appeals on TV ask for money, blankets, clothes for the homeless, and hope it gets where it is most needed. Yet would you believe it, without any of these disasters, there are still hundreds of homeless people in this civilised country. If you wander the streets at night or in the early morning you would see here and there the homeless, those with just a single tattered blanket covering them (and their heads), sleeping stupefied in shop doorways, usually with half-empty cans of Special Brew nearby.

I've seen a bearded young man, with a rucksack containing all his basic needs, leading a loyal dog on his wanderings. He finds shelter at night in doorways, the subway and if weather permits, on a bench in the open. He often gets food at the back of restaurants, their leftovers, and he makes sure his pet companion gets food before him. He snuggles to his dog for warmth at night and not only loves him but needs him, a kind of psychological prop who is a silent comfort, doesn't reject or criticise or complain but recognises him as 'in charge'. The dog seems to understand his own importance to the wandering lonely human. This kind of homeless man is often without ID or National Insurance card, so he wanders from place to place when in actual fact he could get help, but he hates anything to do with authority.

Then you get the teenager who has fallen out with his (or her) parents and leaves home to make for the big city, thinking London is paved with gold. When he does get there he realises the stark reality. If he has any sense he returns home, 'the prodigal son', or if not, he stays and drifts into either crime or prostitution. Of course on rare occasions he/she might find a respectable job, but if these youngsters knew the distress they cause when disappearing without letting parents know that they are all right, they would think twice before absconding.

Without proof of ID, a homeless person who refuses to get help from the social services has to beg for food. A friend of mine told me that she used to help doing voluntary work with an organisation that distributed leftover food from one of the large Marks and Spencer shops. This was handed out to the homeless in the early morning, and they would regularly assemble and wait for this kind hand-out. Some might even stuff some in their pockets to be eaten later on. She remembers one morning to her surprise a regular chap after unwrapping a sandwich, called out, 'Oh no, not salmon again!'

Of course there are voluntary workers and charities trying to get the homeless off the street, there are also hostels, and some organisations can help distraught parents find missing children. On many occasions they have re-united families – a happy ending.

Chapter 96

Old Age

LATER DAYS
The evening is quiet now the gale has gone,
like life when wildness is no more,
for now I see how fondly once I reached
for vanity in youth, those empty quests
that blinded me to Christ.
My soul now housed in body growing old,
raggled by suffering time has wrought
peeps through its shattered walls;
my strength in weakness grows,
the nearer I draw home.
Leaving the past behind I glimpse the new
standing on the threshold of my room with God.

Rev. Waddington Feather (Shrewsbury)

A seven-year-old child, when asked what do you think old age is?, in a sweet childlike voice replied: 'You lose your teeth, you can't hear properly, you need glasses, your skin gets all wrinkly, and your legs get wobbly!' That about sums it up, except the fact that many grannies and grandpas spend time listening and filling a loving gap often forgotten by busy parents. There's the knitting granny supplying all kinds of needed woollies, or the grandpa helping by fetching children from school, not to mention the times when babysitting is on the menu.

Of course, the aches and pains of old age are many, yet this does not mean the elderly are a burden. Many retired folk are engaged in useful voluntary work. To mind comes RSVP (Retired

223

Senior Volunteer Programme), a charity which motivates senior citizens to help little ones in school with reading, amongst other activities on offer. The reading is usually very popular as the elderly person is accepted as a second granny/grandpa and usually asked to school parties, including Christmas do's etc; it enhances an older person's life, being appreciated by young folk and being in their company.

Years ago grannies and grandpas used to be part of the family. Now, when women go to work and everything is rushed in the home and geared to earning money to improve living standards, the old person lives on their own or eventually is admitted to an old people's home, a thing which can be very depressing for relatives and the old person when the decision has to be made.

In my occupation at Waltham Forest Borough Council, some of my visits were to the elderly, which I loved. Here is a report of two of the many visits to elderly people (as reported in my biography).

1. Mr Henry, a sad old man who had lost his wife recently. The only sunshine in his life was a little robin redbreast, who would fly onto his windowsill daily to be fed. I had never seen a little wild bird so tame, nor any man so gentle. How he loved that little bird. There seemed a moving sweet fellowship between them. One day when visiting, I was ushered into the room with 'Hush, hush' and there was the little robin sitting on the windowsill waiting for his 'tit bits'. I stood and watched fascinated as the little bird picked crumbs off Mr Henry's hand. When the little bird flew off, Mr Henry whispered to me, 'I believe this little robin is my beloved Betty come back to comfort me.'

2. Mrs Bridger, a 79-year-old lady, and a lady she surely was, tall, erect and very authoritative. Apparently she had been a Red Cross commandant before retirement and her late husband had been a police inspector. For this reason she was on a very good police widow's pension. She now suffered from mild delusions and refused to pay her rates (now called Council Tax) because she claimed the Queen had absolved her from paying rent and rates due to her services to the country while in the Red Cross. And furthermore, she thought she could not be evicted because she claimed she was a member of the House of Lords. A psychiatrist's report stated:

This lady is suffering from a senile paranoid state, perhaps

224

predominantly an element of dementia. Whilst she is therefore undoubtedly mentally ill, she would not be amenable to outpatient's treatment. As she seems to be coping pretty well caring for herself, admission to a psychiatric hospital is not indicated. I'm sure the best course would be for the Council to turn a blind eye to arrears of rent, and for her to be allowed to stay where she is. If evicted she will almost certainly have to go into a mental hospital, which would be a pity, and of course cost the country far more.

Having had success gaining entry into homes other officials had failed to do, I was designated to visit this formidable lady and persuade her to pay her dues. On my first visit I announced myself as the Queen's representative. I told her (with fingers crossed behind my back) that the Queen sent her regards and was so pleased to hear that Mrs Bridger was contributing towards the nation in spite of having been absolved by Her Majesty (God forgive me). After that, Mrs Bridger paid her rent etc. (God bless her). I did visit this lady regularly to discuss her life achievements as a Red Cross commandant, mostly during the Second World War. She enjoyed my visits, plying me with cups of tea from delicately hand-painted porcelain cups which had seen better days.

I would like to end 'Old Age' with a poem by Susan Glyn:

EARTH AND HEAVEN

In my garden by the sea, I look out on an ocean smooth as ice,
Beyond the flowering tree, my private paradise,
What other glassy sea, unknown could equal this,
What flowers have grown upon the tree of life, flaming with
wilder bliss?
When we move on, leaving this world behind
How can new wine replace a vintage gone? What shall we find?
'You can't take it with you,' say the sages. But, yes we can!
The dreams and memories of all ages,
Can be fulfilled, within the infinite span
Of the 'Many Mansions' Christ prepared for Man.

Chapter 97

Mountain Rescues (Switzerland and Wales)

SWITZERLAND

Whenever I fly back to Switzerland the flight over the mountains never fails to thrill me. Those imposing snow- and ice-bedecked mountain peaks below the circling plane exhibit their silent awesomeness. They were there thousand of years before us and will still be there thousands of years after we are gone. Below, little neutral Switzerland awaits the plane and its occupants.

Switzerland, a little jewel, nestles between Germany, France, Italy and Austria, and is famous for its high mountains. Apart from chocolate, cheese and watches, it is a ski paradise and an adventurous challenge for mountain climbers. Yet in this little beautiful country lie hidden deadly dangers. Skiing, skating and mountaineering are very exhilarating sports but can be hazardous. Many a skier leaves his skiing holidays on crutches with broken limbs. They can be caught in snowstorms or worse, a massive avalanche.

If skating on an icebound lake, the ice may not be thick enough and break, and the skater sink into icy waters. As he tries to get back onto the still icebound parts of the lake, ice breaks off every time he holds onto it to haul himself out. A rescue operation is very difficult, to get a drowning man out of the broken icy water without breaking the ice, the rescuer lies on wooden planks. I remember two boys crossing a small icebound lake. When they got to the middle the ice broke. Luckily they were near a small island and managed, even though water-logged, to get onto dry land and stayed there shivering till rescuers arrived. Never again would they try unknown territory.

When I was barely five years old and still living in a small

Alpine resort, my parents took me to see the devastation caused by an avalanche about three miles from our hotel. An avalanche is like a tsunami, but instead of a gigantic forceful water wave up to 10 feet high, overtaking all in its path, it is a massive, heavy, ice and snow combination hurtling with terrific speed, sometimes nearly half a mile wide, down the mountainside, sucking everything within its path into its turmoil – skiers, animals, trees, mountain chalets. It can cover and devastate whole villages, causing death and destruction. After this avalanche, we could see deer's legs poking out of the snow, broken trees, chalet roofs and chimneys littering the devastated snow-covered land. Rescuers were still busy trying to find survivors while we were there.

Another even more deadly danger is mountain climbing. Many experienced climbers have been killed trying to master difficult and fearsome mountains, some never to be found again, but frozen in an icy gorge. The most notoriously dangerous is the Eiger, its north wall the most deadly to climb. It is one of three mountains next to each other, Jungfrau (Virgin), Monk and Eiger, with the famous Matterhorn just behind. To climb the Eiger to the summit is a achievement coveted by mountaineers all over the world. There are rescue teams stationed in towns and villages around those mountains. As described earlier, the large Swiss-bred woolly Bernardiner dog (St Bernard) is part of some search teams to rescue the lost in the snow. Not all lost climbers can be rescued, if the mission is impossible and putting the rescuers at certain deadly risk the rescue mission is off.

Another memory is when in the 1930s four German climbers got caught in a storm high up on the north wall of the Eiger and were swept off their feet and their safety pitons (iron rods which are driven deep into the ice to hold ropes) torn out of the ice they had hacked them into. For safety's sake all four climbers were attached by a length of rope with enough length in between each man to allow for climbing. Following the man in front, should one man slip or fall the other two would be his safety attachment. But on this occasion, the storm was so terrific the top man was knocked off so violently that he lost his foothold, his iron piton came out and he plunged downwards, dragging the next three climbers, one by one, with him to certain death. The gruesome thing was the reports in the newspapers and photographs of the climbers hanging dead on ropes. They could be seen with binoculars by hundreds of sightseers, till eventually (so I was told) marksmen shot through the top rope, which released the men together into a private dignified cold mountain grave.

With the mountain being 13,000 feet high, a climber nearly at the top could fall a thousand feet and still be very high up on the mountain, his rope held by a jutting out rock, leaving the climber hanging in mid air, a frozen, macabre corpse, for days or even weeks, swaying back and forth with the current of air or wind, till brought down by brave men risking their lives. Today helicopters can take a man off the notorious north face of the Eiger. Up to 1984 approximately 50 experienced mountaineers lost their lives.

Whenever climbers attempted to climb the north wall of the Eiger to the summit, many of the villages like Grindelwald would be packed with visitors, their binoculars tracing the climber's progress or failure, and newspaper photographers reporting to the general public. The numerous telescopes placed in viewing positions (with money slots) were constantly in use, with visitors queuing to get a glimpse of the climber.

WALES

(Contributed kindly by Carol Steadman, one of the voluntary mountain rescue team)

The Brecon Mountain Rescue team is based in the town of Brecon, Powys, in the heart of the Brecon Beacons National Park. The area is visited by thousands of people each year because of its outstanding beauty and the variety of countryside and wildlife. The majority of people who come here have a very pleasant time and return home safely, but the climate in this area is changeable and people can find themselves in difficulties, especially on the mountains (the Brecon Beacons). This can be so serious it could lead to being lost, injured or even to death on the mountains.

The Mountain Rescue team is called out to assist people to safety. Rescues range from lost or injured walkers on the mountain to assisting the police when elderly or vulnerable people go missing. The rescue team deal with a great number of accidents ranging from head, spinal or limb injuries to heart attacks and hypothermia. The police will call the team for help, maybe a person hasn't returned by a specific time, and there is often very little information, so a search is started. When found, the casualty receives a high standard of medical care and the person is carried to the nearest roadside for an ambulance to take them to hospital, or for a helicopter to evacuate the injured person, depending on the seriousness of their injuries.

There are also many calls to search for local people gone missing. The Brecon Beacons, being their back yard, is a huge area to search. They may be elderly or confused people suffering from various forms of ill health or even wanting to commit suicide.

The Mountain Rescue team responds to problems 365 days of the year and 24 hours a day. Sometimes there will be weeks without a call and then three in one day; the work is very unpredictable. Most of the team members have full-time jobs where it would be difficult to just walk out, but from approximately 50 members in the team, several can be sent, and should more be needed, we can call out three other Mountain Rescue teams. Our team too can be called to different areas. We have been called out to assist the Dartmoor team for a search for a large group of young people missing a few years ago.

Reports have to be made of all incidents and injuries, and if death happens, reports become available to the Coroner's Court and police investigations.

All team members have medical training and carry special equipment to assist with resuscitating and warming the injured to make them comfortable until the ambulance or helicopter arrives. A small number of calls end in distressing results; however, the majority of searches end in a loved one being found and treated,

The team members range from 18 to 70 years old and may be called out at any time, day, night or weekends. They leave their families and often go out in appalling weather conditions. The team is called out approximately 50 times a year. All this is voluntary. They have to raise their own funds to keep the team operational to the tune of £18,000 a year.

The Mountain Rescue team are a very special group of people. There are times when not only the casualty, but also individual team members depend on the skills and experience of their colleagues when in a life-threatening situation. In one instance, the team were rescuing a body from a river. The current was so strong, they were in danger of being swept away themselves and their lives were in danger. There is a special trust and respect that has been earned for you to put your confidence in your fellow rescuers.

Working with and as a team makes this work special and satisfying.

Chapter 98

Water and Fire (Good Servants but Bad Masters)

WATER

Chambers Dictionary: '... a clear transparent colourless liquid, perfectly neutral in its reaction, and devoid of taste or smell; any body of this ... such as an ocean, lake, river etc.'

Water, this elusive life maintaining thing you cannot live without. You cannot hold it in your hand; it will trickle through your fingers. If in a glass you can't see it, only through it, it is transparent; it will seep and escape through the smallest crack. It is an essential for maintaining life apart from its constant use in housekeeping, cleaning, cooking etc.

My memory of water's mystery starts high up in the mountains. I remember being taken as a child up to the Rhone Glacier, which apparently is shrinking each year, a large shiny sheet of ice covering the mountainside as though it was protecting its rocks beneath against climbers. A small trickle or rivulet emerged from its mouth, bubbling merrily downwards, picking up other rivulets on its way, becoming a stream which again picked other streams up on its way until it became a river. Most rivers from mountain glaciers find their way eventually into the sea or ocean, sometimes on the way entering a lake and leaving it on its downward way to a turbulent or calm ocean. Waiting there, it will be attracted upwards towards heaven by the sun. Then, forming into clouds, it will return its life-giving properties through rain, to earth, plants and man. In the deep ocean it nourishes and houses fantastic coloured fish, even predators: the feared sharks, the amazing huge whales and the gentle loveable dolphins.

Robin loves a good shower, a swim in a holiday pool, canoeing, or just watching water skiers swishing past.

The darker side of water

We all know the frustration of someone leaving a tap on and then there is a flood in the bathroom. But what about the floods which occur after heavy rainfall? Some unfortunate houses near a river, having been chosen for their lovely view, get flooded time and again if there is heavy downpour, the houses becoming not only unsaleable but eventually uninsurable too. The owners of such properties must live in constant fear of any further heavy rainfall. Nothing can be more distressing than to refurbish a house again and again.

Seventeen years ago I nearly bought such a house by the river near Ross-on-Wye. The fantastic situation of the river and grass edge with trees was a delight to view. The house itself had recently been completely redecorated and refurbished with new kitchen units, a lovely bathroom and impressive oak open staircase to the bedrooms. Everything in excellent order inside and out, the prize, it was well below market price. It was only when a local friend pointed out to me that this house was regularly flooded in unusually heavy rainfall, which could happen every five years or so, that I looked elsewhere (the complete refurbishing of that house must have been after a recent flood). Several houses on this lower stretch of the river were similarly prone to flooding. Of course there is now a law that you have to declare such matters when selling a property.

Then there are the more serious floods like the ones in Lynmouth, years ago, and Boscastle more recently. Both villages were flooded by their usually romantic little rivers which turned into an angry torrent, devastating them after unusually heavy rain. These catastrophes were nothing in comparison to the widespread floods abroad where thousands of people, including children, are made homeless or killed. The worst flood disaster was the tsunami which hit the beautiful holiday island Sri Lanka and nearby islands in Thailand and Indonesia with such unbelievable force and destruction, hurling people, cars, houses and all in its path like toys. The death toll was unbelievable. All we could do was sit and watch with horror on TV and give help freely, which was only a drop in the ocean of the actual need.

FIRE

Candles on birthday cakes and Christmas trees, and a candlelit meal, how romantic! Little children holding candles in a Christingle service is one of the sweetest sights. The friendly glow in a fireplace in winter, warms your heart and soul, and fire cooks your food, making life pleasant. The fantastic displays of fireworks on special occasions fill you with wonder. And a sing song by a camp fire tops it all.

The darker side of fire

But beware, a little match in a little hand can light the beginning of a hungry fire. Houses have been burned to the ground by a careless, still glowing, dropped cigarette. The horrific memory of children burned to death in a fire can never, ever be eradicated and parents for the rest of their lives will ask themselves, Was it our fault? Could it have been avoided?

Then there are the larger fires which not only burn down one house but a whole town or city. To mind springs The Great Fire of London in 1666, which started in Pudding Lane in a baker's shop. The fire took hold so quickly and ferociously it turned London into ashes in four days. In desperation, houses were dynamited in its path in the hope of creating an open barrier the flames would not cross, but cinders flew across and the burning continued. There are stories of how people desperately tried to save some belongings by carrying them on their backs or pushing them in small carts. King Charles II is said to have never left London during the fire, and rolled up his sleeves and helped wherever it was needed, just like a commoner.

Not to leave out the very large fires in Australia which burn acres of bush, woodland and threaten towns, even cities, started by careless picnickers.

So which is more important, fire or water? I think they both are important but water is the more important, as water can put out a fire but fire cannot put out water.

Chapter 99

War and Dictators

WAR

When I look back with horror to 1918 when I was only 18 months old, the baby of a then normal loving family in Switzerland, at that very time in Russia the Tsar and his family were brought down from their upstairs room where they had been imprisoned and all shot in cold blood, one of the most appalling murders in history. As I was being cosseted and spoiled by my three elder sisters, we were unaware of the tragic happenings so near to us.

In my later teens, again living my ordinary life and looking forward to travelling to Britain to learn English, we were unaware of the horrific camps (Dachau and Belsen) only just across the border in Germany and the unbelievable macabre stories emerging of gas chambers and the annihilation of thousands of people, including helpless women and children. All this so near, and we innocently unaware.

When I came to Britain in 1937, according to the media Hitler was a shouting, screaming joke and Churchill a warmonger who warned of an exploding situation. The German national song of that time, 'Deutschland, Deutschland über alles' ('Germany, Germany over all') still rings in my ears with accompanying marching feet.

I remember the then Prime Minister, Neville Chamberlain, with his traditional black umbrella coming back from Germany waving a piece of paper to the media: the alleged signed peace agreement with Hitler. When a year later war broke out, everybody realised the joke: Hitler was the most dangerous maniac and Churchill now became the Prime Minister and a hero leading the war to an eventual victory.

I then saw war at first hand at King's College hospital in London, where bombs and sirens were the order of the day and night. I also spent a year in the sector hospital in Horton near Epsom, and saw the wounds a war inflicts.

Although Switzerland is neutral, my family experienced the war. There was food rationing, as in Great Britain. My sister Emmy married a Swiss man who worked for the Swiss Government. They were stationed in Louvain, Belgium, and had a house there. When the Germans invaded Belgium they escaped into France, leaving all their possessions behind. Then they were stationed in Rouen and set up home for a second time. When the Germans marched into France they uprooted themselves a second time and were sent to Rome, unaware that Rome too was in danger, and they had to leave their home and their belongings a third time and come back to Switzerland, where her husband was put in charge of a very large silo where imported corn was treated so it wouldn't sprout. I remember it being in Brig, right next to the Simplon Tunnel, near the railway station which leads into Italy, whence corn would arrive as Switzerland had insufficient to feed the nation. The silo employed a workforce of 70 and my brother-in-law supervised them. They stayed there till they retired and at last were safe.

Phiny, my other sister, married a German-born man. His mother was a maid in a rich German family and became pregnant by her employer. The baby was adopted by a Swiss family but was promised 20,000 marks (today's equivalent is at least a million pounds) on reaching adulthood. I remember them trying for years to get this money, to no avail. Hitler confiscated it and they never saw a cent of it.

DICTATORS

Hitler was supposed to be Mussolini's friend, but in reality each was jealous and tried to outdo each other. Both came to a very sticky end. Hitler killed himself with Eva Braun, his mistress, whom he married at the last moment, and Mussolini's body with that of his mistress was paraded hanging upside down through the streets. Mussolini did not marry his mistress because he was already married.

WAR CASUALTIES

Nobody wins a war. The thousands of lives lost can never be replaced. It takes years to rebuild towns and cities. The aftermath: the crippled, disabled and mentally affected are forgotten. After the Falklands war, soldiers claimed abnormalities that affected their offspring were the result of anti-disease injections received, which altered their genes. Some sued the Government. The compensation culture was unheard of after the Second World War; at any rate, when thousand of young men had died, you were lucky to come out of it alive, never mind the condition.

The Second World War not only affected the countries involved but other countries near them, including neutral Switzerland, which had to call up its young able men to protect and guard the frontiers. All major passes through mountains were dynamited ready to be blown up should anyone try and invade the country. Further north, by Basel, the river Rhine with its strong current seemed impassable and a national protection barrier; the rest of the frontiers were manned. My father too was called up.

Switzerland does not have an army ready at hand, but has conscription where every young man reaching 18 years of age has to train initially (I believe it is for six months) to an expected grade and then follows it up with an annual three-week refresher course, to be ready, should a war take place, to protect Switzerland's neutrality. Firms and employers know that this three weeks' absence is of national importance, and it is accepted as part of the employment contract. My nephew told me he thought it was this training which made a man of him. (Pity it can't be implemented in every country, it might curb hooliganism.)

In spite of the wars raging around Switzerland, it stayed free through the past two world wars, it gave sanctuary to many escaped prisoners of war and The Red Cross is stationed and functions within its safe frontiers.

Chapter 100

Robin's Autistic Home and its Residents

> The earthly beauty I can feel and see,
> other people's way is not for me
> nor their race for fame's message
> nor treading on this difficult passage,
> I watch through an enclosed psychological cage,
> I've escaped love's triangles and this generation's wild rage.

I know some of the residents in Robin's home. There is lovable Martin, whose huge tummy is usually exposed to all and sundry it appears to be too large to stay in a tee shirt. He walks around touching people and objects gently as though to make sure they're real. Thomas is thin and fairly good-looking. He does attempt to talk to you, all smiles, usually repeats everything you say, and likes shaking your hand. Then there is James, a very tall and handsome young man, another anxious mother's son, who often runs around in the grounds regardless of the weather, waving his arms around. (Don't forget, they all have a mother, whose only wish is for their son to be like others, normal. But then what is normal?)

One day as I was coming along in the grounds of Longford Court, James came running and shouting, stopped right in front of my 5 foot 2 frame and looked down at me. I stood my ground and said, 'Hallo James, my name is Dorothea.' He stood very still, searching my face, and I repeated, 'I'm Dorothea. Please say D-o-r-o-th-e-a.' He looked puzzled. I said again, 'Say D-O-R-O-TH-EA,' then he slowly said, 'D-o-r-th-ea!' I was thrilled and said, 'Well done, James.' I believed I had made a little bond with him; he is able to communicate a little in his own difficult way. It seems strange but I love these autistic boys more than some of the world-renowned stars, and of course my Robin is one of them.

To have a conversation with the other residents seems unlikely, but Robin can compensate by talking to staff, and of course the close relationship with his key therapy worker is of vital importance to him. The staff are all experienced people and skilled in caring for autistic people, unlike the other three previous homes Robin was resident in. In this home I feel confident that he is all right and he is treated like an adult young man, though he is a child in a man's body. Carers who look after people with this kind of disability are the salt of the earth and should all have special medals, but just as dedicated as they are, so they are all also very modest people in a world where only fame and fortune seem to count.

Chapter 101

Great Men and Women

We've seen them on TV and to mind comes the inexperienced young man now remembered as 'Eddie The Eagle' who dared the ski slopes and the high jump which is only usually attempted by experienced skiers. He dared, and in front of a gasping crowd not only attempted the jump but landed right way up on his skis and finished the course. Was this a one-off? We hardly heard of him again.

Then I was lucky enough to turn on my TV in the 1950s when Professor Carl Gustav Jung, the eminent psychiatrist, gave the only interview on television while visiting London. He cured many people of mental illness and believed in the power of dreams and wrote many books on mental ill health. Although having been born, brought up and educated in Switzerland, he travelled abroad, especially to Africa, and was a strong believer in fairness and people's rights. He campaigned strongly against apartheid. In the interview on that day, he was in his eighties, a tall, still good-looking, white-haired, dignified man. At the end of the interview the reporter asked Professor Jung, 'Do you believe in God?' Professor Jung looked at the young reporter with a benign smile and said slowly, 'I don't believe. I know.' He was one of those great men recognising there was a power greater than themselves.

Gandhi, the famous Indian guru (not a Christian) was reported to have said. 'There is an undeniable, mysterious power that pervades every thing, I feel it, I do not see it; it is this unseen power which makes itself felt and yet defies all proof, because it is so unlike all that I perceive through my senses. There is an unalterable law governing everything or every being that exists or lives. The law then which governs life is God. Law and law giver are one.'

239

Another of his sayings was: 'It is better in prayer to have a heart without words, than words without a heart.'

Little things great men don't mind doing: The professor I knew who got on his hands and knees to help children pick up spilled sweets at a church party. Dr Wright, Waltham Forest MOH in the 1970s, who chaired an important meeting on health with councillors and council dignitaries wearing an appalling garish tie, explaining with an apologetic smile: 'I have to wear this. If I don't, there will be hell to pay. My children gave this to me for my birthday!' (His children were still under school age.)

Great women who come to mind are Florence Nightingale, Mother Teresa, and Gladys Aylward, who ferried children to safety through wartorn, dangerous territory in China. The first of the two matrons under whom I trained was Miss M.K. Blyde, OBE, at King's College hospital. She earned her OBE for services in the war and she was an outstandingly good matron, not only to the nurses but to the young students. She was kind, understanding, yet firm and respected. The other was Miss Wearn, the matron in charge of the district nurses' training centre in Leyton, where I did my district training in the 1950s. After we passed our exams she said, 'Now girls, in getting your coveted Queen's district nurses badge, don't let it go to your head. Remember you are public servants and paid by the tax payer.' And she added with a wicked smile, 'And if you would like to know, this goes also for doctors and consultants, though they don't always seem to realise it.'

Of course there are thousands of great men and women helping this world to be a better place, some famous, some never heard of, some of lowly birth, some kings and queens.

Chapter 102

Dreams

I have a dream! *Martin Luther King*

His dream was of a world being free of apartheid so all men no matter what colour could be brothers: a dream which is coming to pass, by and by, since his sad assassination. There are two kinds of dreams, wishful ones (reverie) that do not always come true, and real dreams which may be nightmares. Dreams, like astrology, have been used for centuries to interpret the future. Carl Gustav Jung used real dreams to treat and even cure mentally disturbed patients. He wrote many books on the subject.

My friend Nancy told me she used to have a recurring dream about when the children were small and happy in their first house. I too had a recurring dream years back when only five years old, when we lived in the Alps and were still a family, about our musical gatherings. This dream later was replaced by me always being lost somewhere, or being in an embarrassing circumstance, like finding myself in only pyjamas in church in the middle of a service, surrounded by parishioners, trying hard to hide myself and searching for my clothes under the pew. I wonder what Dr Jung would have made of that dream?

Do autistic people have dreams? I asked Robin, and the conversation went like this:

'Do you have dreams, Robin?'

'Yes.'

'What are they?'

'I don't know.'

'Can't you remember?'

'No!'

241

'Were they nice dreams?'

'Yes.'

'Do you like having dreams?'

'Yes.'

Could it be that autistic people can dream, fly freely, become normal and see this world's wonders and nature in their dreams and so compensate for their caged abilities? I also wonder, do animals dream? Our dog Prince definitely did. He would be stretched out in front of the fire fast asleep and suddenly start to whimper and his legs would twitch and move back and forth as though he was running. I'm sure he was dreaming, chasing something, perhaps a rabbit? None of the cats we had over the years showed such symptoms. They always looked very relaxed when asleep – unless they were having happy dreams of just sleeping and letting the world go by.

Chapter 103

Dyslexia

Chambers Dictionary: 'word blindness, great difficulty in learning to read or spell, unrelated to intellectual competence and of unknown cause.'

Bailliere's Nurses' Dictionary: not listed.

Obviously this condition was not recognised in 1940 and those children so afflicted would have been thought to be simple. But they are not retarded in any way and some become quite brilliant in later life. Dear friends of mine had an only child, a lovely little girl who appeared bright and actively happy. She could sing and dance and recite nursery rhymes which her mother had taught her. Then she joined school. Slowly her happy self changed, she became withdrawn and moody and the school reports stated that she lagged behind the other pupils. The parents were devastated. What was the reason? Why had their seemingly bright little girl changed so dramatically?

Her mother had been reading stories to her from an early age, which this child loved, and as she could recite every nursery rhyme, there was nothing wrong with her memory. In mental arithmetic, too, the child excelled, but failed to understand the written-down questions. It was after frantic visits to social workers, councillors and doctors that eventually she was diagnosed dyslexic. This made sense to the parents, and the mother started to help with homework by reading questions out, so her daughter could answer them, and the mother wrote them down. Once diagnosed, the little girl got special help in school and now kept up with her peers. Her moods disappeared. This not only brought back the happy, loveable child but lifted an intolerable worry from the parents.

To be suffering from dyslexia, especially if undiagnosed, is a heavy burden for any child. The child realises she is different from the other children and tries hard to keep in step but gets frustrated, not knowing what is wrong. Sometimes dyslexic children are even taunted by other children. They have been known to struggle for years undiagnosed, thinking themselves inferior to their classmates, their self-confidence eventually shattered. Nowadays, luckily, the condition has been recognised and treatment is available. Very often children with dyslexia have another brilliant streak to compensate for this unfortunate condition and frequently attain senior positions in life.

Chapter 104

Phobias

Chambers Dictionary: '**phobia** ... a fear, aversion or hatred, *esp* a morbid and irrational one'.

Bailliere's Nurses' Dictionary: 'fear or obsession'.

My first encounter with a phobia was when my five-year-old daughter Pat would not go to bed because she thought there was a spider hiding in it. No matter what I said, she persisted and shrank away from going to bed. The only way to reassure her was to change the sheets and shake them and the pillows in front of her. Then she settled down and all seemed well, until her seven-year-old sister, with whom she shared the bedroom, whispered, 'Spider, spider,' and the whole process started again. After I reprimanded the teasing, mischievous sister and changed the bed again, she settled down and peace reigned. I then caught a spider at random and held it in my clasped hand, just to show Pat what a little helpless creature it really was, and she stopped worrying about spiders for good.

The next encounter of a phobia was in Merthyr Tydfil. I had a young couple living next door with their young son. One day the mother came rushing over in panic. 'Can you help? There's a spider on my curtains.' I went over, feeling very honoured to be called for such a task. Stepping on a chair I picked up the 'monster' in front of the little awed audience, took it and threw it into the next-door garden, telling them that I never killed spiders as they got rid of nasty bluebottles. I was called only once more. Maybe they got used to spiders after seeing me actually pick one up without coming to harm.

There was a woman who had a dirt phobia. Her house was so spotless she even ran behind you with a mop, wiping wherever you stepped in case you left footmarks. This phobia was so strong it lost her many friends and even broke up her marriage eventually and made her a nervous wreck.

Phobias to do with fear of certain creatures are easily solved. The child was introduced to a large hairy spider and eventually persuaded to touch it, then even hold it. And the young woman who nearly fainted when seeing only pictures of a snake was taken to a zoo and could look at a large snake coiled round the keeper's neck without hurting him. In fact the keeper seemed to love to show off his pet charge. She too was persuaded to touch the 'beast', stroke its head and hold its tail.

There are more serious phobias which may cause years of misery and only be resolved after counselling. One woman wouldn't leave her house for 20 years. Her phobia was people, traffic and street noise. She first emerged from isolation on the counsellor's arm, treading gingerly out to her dreaded world to test the water, as the saying goes. Then eventually she gained confidence and after weeks she eventually even dared to go shopping.

Chapter 105

Fertility Versus Infertility

Fertility

The arrival of a wanted and awaited precious baby is one of the most wonderful gifts of human experience, not only for the mother; the first baby cry in the delivery room always thrills all those involved with the birth.

Fertility is a blessing from God: 'And God blessed them, and God said unto [Adam and Eve] be fruitful, and multiply, and replenish the earth' (Genesis 1.28). The problem began with overpopulation, as in China and Africa, where population exceeded the ability to feed a multitude where the majority of land is desert or jungle, unsuitable to grow crops.

In the West the problem was of a different kind. The rich managed some birth control, the poor had too many babies. The mother was worn out by yearly childbirth and the worry of further pregnancies was a constant threat. In the 1940s, the Family Planning clinics opened their doors to ordinary people and gave advice, and certain pregnancy-stopping devices. They did prevent some pregnancies but were not 100 per cent effective. I worked evenings for two years at a Family Planning clinic. The Pill came in in the 1950s and then instead of teaching women how to insert their barrier devices we started to teach them how and when to use the Pill. So the norm today is to plan your family, and most families have two children. There are still some families with three or more offspring, but they are in the minority. A family here in Britain was reported to have 11 children and the mother said she wanted more as she 'just could not be without a baby in the house'. The house must have been run like a hotel and no doubt the older

247

children helped with the younger ones. The mother when interviewed appeared relaxed and happy, cuddling her latest arrival. To her the family was a full-time job which had to be organised 'military fashion' for its smooth running.

Infertility

Infertility too was present in the Old Testament. Abraham's wife was barren... But in her old age 'God opened her womb...' To yearn for a baby is natural, an instinct; even in childhood, playing with dolls makes little girls happy. Dressing, bathing and pushing little dolls' prams is preparation for later motherhood. But when the need for a baby is denied to parents, the deep yearning increases with time and becomes more desperate each month when the menstrual cycle keeps repeating. The man feels he is inadequate and the woman feels that nature has denied her the right to motherhood. Her sorrow and yearning are deep and whenever she sees children playing or hears their laughter her heart trembles. Seeing babies in prams gives her an urge to pick the baby up and hug it, but of course it is not her baby. It has been known for a frustrated woman even to steal a baby from an unattended pram in desperation, take it home, care for it and, when found, land herself in court for abduction, the baby being returned to its shocked mother.

Then there are the barren, unhappy women where the husband needs an heir. King Henry VIII divorced one of his wives for that very reason and Napoleon's passionate love for Josephine culminated in divorce for the same reason. Luckily, nowadays technology is advanced and can treat infertility and the success rate is high. What with *in vitro* fertilisation, etc., infertile couples have hope now. I am not going into the different fertility treatments, their cost, the involvement expected of each man and woman and the time it takes, as there are many very detailed books on the subject, Anna Furse's *The Infertility Companion* (HarperCollins) being one.

Not only women suffer when a baby is denied, some men too long to father a child. Even disabled people yearn to have a baby and I know of a blind woman who, with the help of her husband, cared for her child quite adequately. And lastly, to my great surprise,

Robin asked me one day, 'When can I have a girl friend and baby?' Do autistic people yearn for parenthood? We will never know what goes on in their caged, enclosed minds.

Chapter 106

Cot Deaths

Cot deaths have been much in the news lately. This distressing tragedy seems to be of unknown cause. All kind of things have been blamed: smoking by parents, having a baby with you in your bed and it being smothered accidentally or the baby getting covered in his cot by his own blanket These are only some of the suggestions.

In the 1960s a niece of mine already had two little girls, and when the third baby, a boy, arrived the joy was great. At six months, to her horror and deep sorrow, this baby died in mysterious circumstances. The mother had him in bed with her, as she had done with her other two children when they were babies. This was to have the baby near her to comfort him, rather than having to get up time and again in the night when he cried. So what went wrong? The loss of this baby boy was something the family could never forget. The hurt to these parents and the two little girls who'd wished for a little baby boy lasted for the rest of their lives. Had this baby lived, he would now have been in his forties, a man who would be a support and joy to his parents and sisters.

If on top of this tragedy a mother is accused of killing her baby wilfully, the trauma is unimaginable. It has happened more than once and these poor mothers, grieving for the loss of a child, then faced the ordeal of a court case. Some mothers have even been imprisoned and were cleared only after their family's constant protest and the help of their solicitors. Only the persistent support of a loving husband and relations and constant complaints to authorities eventually cleared these mothers. Apparently some of the diagnostic tests carried out by medical professionals were faulty. These doctors too must carry the guilt of their flawed tests with them, having caused havoc and unhappiness to families in their

250

care. One such mother lost three babies, and later a known clinical cause was diagnosed. So, in spite of desperately wanting a child, she said she was 'afraid of having any more babies'. Adoption or surrogacy was the only other option for her. Infanticide (the killing of a baby) does occur, but very rarely.

Chapter 107

Sport and The Disabled

Sport is something some disabled people love and excel at. To mind comes Tanni Grey Thomson in a wheelchair bringing home a gold medal from the Olympic Games. Then there are frequent wheelchair races, table tennis and swimming displays on our screens to delight us. There is a few minutes' basketball display starter for BBC programmes. These events give the disabled performers a feeling of achievement.

Robin too loves sport and played badminton with the locals in Llechryd. Not only did he play well but he enjoyed it. He played and won often at table tennis and snooker in the local social club for the disabled. I took him swimming once a week, which he again loved, and he sampled the water chute without fear. The thing he liked most was the riding with the disabled once a week, when we would trot through the country side, beside babbling brooks and through little forests.

When we came to Merthyr, swimming was the first sport we enjoyed. We loved the swimming pool at Aberdare. When he was at Thomastown House (in 1998) I found that there was a riding stable in the Country Park in Aberdare, only five miles from our house. Wonderful, I thought. I phoned them and told them that Robin, with me as companion, used to ride with the disabled in Cardigan. Did they have a service for the disabled to ride? 'Yes,' they said. 'Bring him along this afternoon, we'd be delighted to have you.' I was so pleased and when I collected Robin for the day, I told him we were going riding. He looked forward to it eagerly. I also told Thomastown House staff that I was going to take Robin riding to the Aberdare Country Park. We drove there and presented ourselves as arranged. The person in charge asked

252

our name and when we told her, she said quite curtly, 'We're full up.' Not a sorry or any explanation:or why only this morning they had said they would be delighted to see us. Robin kept asking why were we leaving, he wanted to have a ride.

I was devastated and puzzled and took him home. I came to the conclusion it had something to do with Thomastown House. Surely they wouldn't stop Robin and me from riding? Or would they? I remembered one of the temporary workers who only came in occasionally had said to me, 'I was told to beware of Robin, but when there I wondered why, as he seemed all right to me!' I came to the conclusion they thought Robin to be a dangerously mentally ill young man and broadcast it to all and sundry. I may be wrong, but if so, where did it originate? The bush telegraph from Carmarthen?

I was now very angry and decided Robin would ride without telling Thomastown House. I phoned a riding stable in Brecon and they said they had no sessions for disabled but were having a session for beginners on this very Saturday. We went and there was no problem in accepting us both and we duly set off with another group of people. Robin enjoyed it, so did I for the first half-hour, but then we went on and on and I began to feel uncomfortable having been used to only half an hour to one hour but not more. This ride lasted over two hours and when we eventually came back to the stables I was so rigid I couldn't even get off the horse (I was then in my 81st year). Two men had to lift me off the horse and I just collapsed on the ground, my legs like jelly. They carried me, my legs still in sitting position, just the way I had sat on the horse – not a very dignified process. They took me to a bench and sat me down, hoping that in a little time I would get back to normal. All this time Robin had been completely all right and had enjoyed every minute of his ride, and he just stood by, a little confused at my condition, and waited for me to recover the use of my legs. So I'm afraid that was the end of riding for Robin as I could not let him go on his own.

Chapter 108

For Whom the Bell Tolls: Death

Death comes to all of us sooner or later and leaves our loved ones behind grieving. I have not had the experience of a member of my family dying while I was present as I was abroad, though I visited my mother in hospital just before she died. I was her fourth daughter and she had always wanted a boy. The first baby was a boy but he died at birth. So I brought Christopher, my six-month-old son, to the hospital and laid him next to her, which made her very happy. Unfortunately I had to return to Britain before she died but went back for the funeral.

My first experience of death was when I was 10 years old. In Zurich there is a wooden covered bridge over the river Limat in the middle of town. Four men were working under it doing repairs. They were in a boat attached to the bridge's main beams. The boat overturned and the men fell into the torrent. Three were rescued, but the fourth got his feet entangled in weeds and was held fast. A crowd stood watching, horrified. I was amongst them and saw the man underwater as though he was standing upright but bending slightly forward, his hair waving with the downward flow of the river. People were watching, praying, willing for the man to be rescued. By the time the first three men were rescued, the fourth was dead, still attached by his feet to the weeds, still upright, to the distress of the people watching. He was eventually freed and brought out of the river. Women were crying, and I was deeply affected and have never forgotten this terrible accident.

I experienced death as a nurse many times and each time was deeply affected and felt for the grieving relatives. Often the death was a relief after months of a painful illness. But there are deaths which affect the whole hospital. We had a young mother ready to

254

be delivered of her baby. She was advised by the gynaecologist to have a Caesarean section as her pelvic bone structure was very narrow. She refused, she wouldn't hear of it. She wanted to have the baby the normal way and experience the birth fully. She died on the delivery table. Her little baby boy lived. I forever see the gynaecologist in despair, standing in the delivery room with bent head after all the desperate attempts at life-saving had failed. No one can imagine how the loss of a young mother affects every staff member and the rest of the hospital. We cared for the baby for three weeks, and then the father came to collect his motherless son.

Not much later, the opposite happened. A woman who had aborted time and time again was admitted to be monitored during this latest pregnancy. She suffered from diabetes and to complicate matters further had two uteruses. This would be operated on after the birth, but she would not be able to have another baby. She came near to term and the Caesarean was performed. It was a lovely baby – Caesarean babies always are. As they do not have to pass through a narrow birth canal, their heads are beautifully shaped right from the start. Baby and mother were doing fine. The next few days were full of joy for her and her husband. At last they had the baby they had longed for for such a long time. A few days later I went off duty and when I came back I was told the baby had suddenly turned blue and, despite all the desperate efforts by doctors and nurses to save it, the baby died. The whole hospital seemed to be in mourning.

Then there was the 18-year-old young man with a rheumatic heart condition. To listen to the thumping of his poor heart through a stethoscope was frightening. Once I passed his bed and he grabbed hold of my hand and whispered, 'When I get out of here, will you go out with me?' I said half-heartedly, 'Yes.' 'Promise?' he insisted. 'Yes,' I said. He died three days later. In those days, he would have been given a new heart, but today he would have been given antibiotics and not got a rheumatic heart.

Another death which stays in my memory is of a 60-year-old man who, apart from diabetes, suffered from other complaints. It was Christmas Day and the ward was decorated with balloons, a Christmas tree and colourful tinsel hanging from the ceiling. One of the senior consultants, wearing a chef's hat and apron, was carving the turkey and amongst all this Christmas hubbub the man sat up in bed, spread his arms out wide with joy and died.

In another ward a delicately beautiful eighteen-year-old girl was dying with miliary TB, a terminal illness as the bug is in the bloodstream. Of course there were many more deaths, just as there were many cures and many newborn babies going home with happy parents.

One of the most pathetic funerals I attended was one financed by Waltham Forest Borough Council. A very old and shaky man's wife had died. He had not the resources for a funeral, neither would he attend as he was too upset and anyway had not got, as he put it, the honourable clothes to wear. We offered to rig him out but he refused; 'I shall break down. I'm sorry, I just can't face it.' So the borough commissioned me to attend as their representative. This was over 30 years ago and all I remember was the coffin being placed at table height in a remote chapel with only a small flower wreath on top supplied by the borough. A priest or vicar read a short address and there was only me and one other man (a relative?). He did not introduce himself. We stood either side of the coffin. It was all so eerie and sad. I did shed a tear for the poor old lady alone in the coffin and almost alone at her funeral except for me and the stranger. I shook hands with him when leaving and he thanked me for coming.

I did go back to visit the old man and told him it had been a beautiful funeral.

Chapter 109

Fame Versus Infamy

FAME

We would all like to be famous and many young people will go through hell and high water to achieve it. Fame? There's a price to be paid. When I watch some of the TV programmes with eager teenagers and even children going through auditions for the glamorous pop world, I see them being shamefully put down then as out of a hundred only a few are chosen, which leaves the rest feeling inferior and frustrated. Some of these youngsters could have been excellent in some other occupation but have been brainwashed by the media, and sometimes eager parents are seduced by glimpses of famous people's fabulous lifestyles. As well as being in front of three or four judges, the nervous contestants know they are being watched by one half of the world. If they are unsuccessful, it could give them an inferiority complex for the rest of their lives. Only a few reach the top and even then to hang on may be nerve-racking. Instant fame like Charlotte Church's and a few others' is rare. Even when the top is reached, you may be only a one-day-wonder and forgotten the next. The real lasting successful people can be counted on your hands. People who had been pressurised while children and have reached the top are not always happy and may even be damaged, as we can see from sad examples like Michael Jackson. And those who truly are famous and rich are constantly under the media's eyes, sometimes being so harassed and chased by the paparazzi that it could even lead to death, as with the Princess of Wales. They have to be careful even on holidays and cannot let their hair down, The media with their long-range lenses are hiding everywhere. Their houses have to be fitted

257

with the most expensive security systems to guard their possessions. They need to look over their shoulders constantly and even need security guards and minders for their children in case there is an intended kidnapping for ransom. So, by the grace of God, my Robin and the other autistic boys are in the home where, in spite of their disability, they are unpressurised and doing the little jobs allocated to them quietly without harassment, led by dedicated carers, men and women. And no one with evil intentions even thinks of them.

INFAMY

To mind spring Dick Turpin, Bonnie and Clyde and others whom Hollywood has glamorised. Of course there are infamous people who horrify us, like Dr Crippen, the first murderer caught by wireless telegraphy as he was making his getaway by ship, Jack the Ripper, who stalked London to kill prostitutes, and Dr Shipman, who murdered over 200 of his elderly patients. Then there are even presidents who became laughing stocks when their infidelity was exposed, and countless MPs who have fallen from great heights due to their extra-marital affairs.

Happy is the little, unheard-of man as he reads his newspaper eagerly and marvels at the world's well-known making fools of themselves.

Chapter 110

Disabled Countries Versus the Affluent West

How do we feel, those of us with cars, washing machines, microwaves and all the other household conveniences, when we read about the famine and devastation caused by natural disasters in other countries? Do we feel guilty when slipping into our warm beds at night? The food left on our plates could feed a starving child for a day. The overweight person, instead of expensive 'tummy tuck' surgery, could eat less and send the money saved to Oxfam or any other charity.

AFRICA

Poverty and famine are rampant in Africa. We know about the crisis in Ethiopia and the way help was given by the efforts of Bob Geldof and other 'showbiz' personalities. We see poor starved babies suckling empty breasts, children with bulging starved stomachs, flies on their faces. Yet money seems to be available for internal wars: mere children are trained with weapons and dictators live in luxury, and their armies well clad and fed.

INDIA

In 1937 an earthquake killed thousands and devastated the land. Three years later a famine killed over three million people and a cyclone in 1967 once more caused devastation and death.

Then there was the 2004 tsunami horror in the Far East. We saw images of this incredible huge, frightening, 10-foot wave rolling

259

towards the shore, with people running frantically, yet being caught in its strong current and being tossed about like leaves in the wind. Houses, cars and debris floated like toys. People clung to trees or anything stable to save themselves. Babies were swept out of their parents' arms. This not only affected the local people but also hundreds of people from this country who were holidaying there. This brought the grief and horror right back into our own midst. It makes our floods seem so minor compared to these enormous disasters

These are disabling, strong, natural forces, and who are the carers? People like you and me who contribute to the charities helping these countries in their distress. The tsunami disaster brought in millions of pounds and hundreds of blankets and clothes collected by voluntary organisations. We do care. Then there are people like Mother Teresa and many more who bravely go to these countries and give their services.

But when you consider our land is green and pleasant, with no tsunamis, cyclones or serious earthquakes, it is not surprising that people from these stricken places want to come here and make a living in a safe place.

Chapter 111

Sunburn, Sunstroke and Melanoma

These conditions were little heard of in the Victorian days or even in the 1940s. A pale delicate skin was the fashion. Pretty hats and lace trimmed parasols were the norm. Today's flimsy clothing 'revealing all' would have been shameful. But the young people of today love to expose a golden and shapely body and go to all kinds of lengths to achieve it, such as sessions even in the winter in a solarium and applying fake tans – which, luckily, are waterproof so you can go swimming and in case of a shower of rain you will not be turned into a streaky zebra.

SUNBURN

Chambers Dictionary: 'reddening of the skin and tenderness caused by excessive exposure to the sun's ultraviolet rays; tanning of the skin'.

Bailliere's Nurses' Dictionary: 'a dermatitis due to exposure to the sun's rays, causing burning and redness'.

This can happen so easily when going to the seaside for the first time in the year after winter and spring. The children, full of joy, play unconcerned with flimsy bathing suits in the full sun. Then comes the pay off, a night of fretting with red hot burning of back and shoulders and excruciating pain. The night is spent by a worrying parent applying calamine lotion. It can happen to anyone who has not taken the precaution of applying a high-factor cream.

SUN STROKE

Chambers Dictionary: 'a medical condition of general collapse caused by prolonged exposure to intense sunlight, which can result in delirium, convulsions and coma'.

Bailliere's Nurses' Dictionary: 'overwhelming prostration caused by exposure to excessive heat from the sun. It is characterised by headache, vomiting, mental confusion and fever or even hyper pyrexia'.

Sunstroke is much more serious than sunburn and hospitalisation may be necessary. It can ruin a holiday, especially if abroad where the sun is much stronger than in Britain. Apart from bringing a much saved for holiday to a drastic end, if uninsured, the cost can be terrific.

MELANOMA

Chambers Dictionary: 'any skin tumour consisting of melanin-pigmented cells; also **malignant melanoma**, a malignant tumour consisting of melanin-pigmented cells which usually develops from a mole and metastasises rapidly'.

Bailliere's Nurses' Dictionary: 'melanotic sarcoma, a form of malignant growth with black pigment (melanin) in it'.

Melanoma, the dangerous skin disease due to overexposure to the sun, is now a condition much in the news and is a shocking price to pay for trying to obtain that longed-for golden tan. Young people seem to be the vulnerable ones. And warnings are now in the media hoping to alert people to this danger. There can be nothing as sad as for a parent to see a lovely young person with a golden tan being afflicted with cancerous melanoma. The price may even be death.

Chapter 112

Memories

Memories sweet or memories bad.
All the memories I ever had,
Are written forever on my heart.

Does an autistic person remember things? Robin does, like when his elder brother took him to see the film *The Great Escape*. He enjoyed it so much; he tried to write it down in his muddled way, time and again. It illustrates that when a family member cares and bothers to take a disabled young man like Robin out, the enjoyment is deeper and the matter in hand better understood. He also used to love the TV programme *On the Buses*, and to this day can still imitate Blakey, the bus driver, absolutely including the way Blakey's lower jaw vibrated with his nasty laugh.

This is on the happy side, yet he still remembers the bullying at Chingford comprehensive school, over 30 years later (see Chapter 2). I believe he only mentions it to me as it was in the past and he thought I should have the answer, or maybe deep in his mind he even blamed me for not helping when it happened and so keeps on reminding me. I shall never know.

What about the other boys in the home, or other autistic people? Perhaps some of their strange behaviour like avoiding certain tasks could be because it reminds them of an unhappy occurrence in the past. The misery of a severely autistic young man in his enclosed mind is unsolvable.

My own happiest memories are when five years old – our family still happily together in our hotel amongst the mountains – roaming freely, with other children gathering wild strawberries in season and blueberries late August and picking beautiful Alpine flowers,

263

like the dark blue gentian violets, paddling in ice cold mountain streams and chasing butterflies. The only recollection of my father was him chasing me upstairs for fun and my mother sitting on a chair on top of a table (would you believe it) mending things while a maid was cleaning the floor underneath (as mentioned in an earlier chapter). The happiest time was when my mother took me on a holiday, just her and me, walking in lovely Swiss countryside surrounded by snow-bedecked mountains, singing to me. This was the last time I saw her happy as the family split up soon after that.

My nursing years were full of happy memories and unhappiness when death occurred. I never gave up on any patient and always, even when they were near death's door, still hoped for a last miracle. The work in hospital gave me a lot of satisfaction and I felt honoured to be involved in this profession. So I look back on those years with only fondness.

Chapter 113

Go Fly a Kite

Let your kite fly high,
Let it soar up into the sky.
Let your soul and spirit
Freely fly along with it.

Geoff was the children's father. He had left us and I was a single mother. He sent us details of some free self-catering holiday accommodation which was available for the benefit of the railway's employees. He was at that time the editor of a monthly railway magazine. The holiday was in an adapted railway carriage in a siding near the proper railway in Dawlish, Devonshire. I went for a fortnight with the two boys, Christopher and Robin. The railway runs alongside the sea so we were quite near the beaches. The problem was, trains kept roaring past near us. First you could hear their distant *chug, chug* noise coming with increased volume as the train came nearer, then an almighty roar, which slowly diminished till it got lost in the distance. This would happen every hour or so and several times in the night. We did get used to it. As for me, it was a minor distraction, having been in London during the war with sirens and bombing going on. The boys usually fell asleep as soon as tucked in, being tired out by the fresh sea air.

One day Chris went fishing with another boy and Robin, who was always wanting to have a kite, made me buy one, and off we two went to a beach where there seemed some wind. Robin was eager to fly his kite. There were other boys with kites, and their dads, all trying to master this sport. Their kites flew high and they were running and shouting with joy following their kite's flight. I tried and tried but our kite just would not fly. It might take off a little, then land straight down again. Robin was then only 10 years old. I so much wanted to start the kite off into the sky and wind and for him to hold the string and manoeuvre it like the other boys. He was so eager, but it just would not fly, I could not understand why. I could decorate walls, paint the outside of the house, do gardening, even change an electric plug (but must confess I nearly blacked out my neighbours when using the Black and Decker drill near an electric cable) but I could not fly a kite.

Robin was very disappointed, so was I, and we went back, Robin dejected, me frustrated, to our holiday train carriage. After the boys had gone to sleep I sat thinking. The fathers we watched were equally excited with their flying kites as their boys and had run and shouted and helped to manoeuvre their flying toy, a shared joy. That is what fathers should be doing, helping to fly a kite, letting it soar, a life symbol of everything else they should be doing for their sons, flying high, being there for them when needed, not only giving an expert hand but teaching them at the same time to create the future man. I could see Robin's disappointed face as we tied up our unsuccessful kite and walked away. I sat in the dark in our holiday railway carriage for a long time, feeling very sad and very low, and every now and then another train roared by. It seemed a long night. Life was roaring past too – no kite, no flying high, no soaring spirit reaching into the clouds.

Whenever I see a flying kite, this holiday picture comes into my mind and I still wish, 'If only I could have got that kite to fly...'

Chapter 114

Bankruptcy

I should know. It happened to my family. The small hotel we had
went bankrupt in the 1920s. We were only one of many small
hotels which suffered this fate after the First World War. It not
only divided our family but smashed it to smithereens. Suddenly
my world fell apart: my home gone, my parents split up, an unheard-
of thing in those days. I was only seven years old at the time and
was ushered to Berne to an aunt, while all our goods and chattels
were assessed and auctioned off to pay some of the debts. My
sisters had left home by this time.

All I gathered from them was that what happened was a shame
on us and it was best not to talk about it.

I spent approximately two years with my aunt. When my uncle
was alive they lived in Argentina, with the Swiss diplomatic service,
she would tell me, in a place called Buenos Aires. This name
haunts me as being the most fantastic, beautiful place in the world,
according to my aunt, who constantly referred to it as the place
where they lived like a king and queen and would have stayed for
ever had not my uncle died. She had brought many lovely trinkets
with her and guarded them like a lioness guarding her cubs. The
other thing she had brought with her was tomato seeds, which she
planted and grew in her conservatory. I had not seen tomatoes
before and was enthralled by them when fully grown. I don't know
which year tomatoes were introduced commercially into Switzerland.
My aunt and her grown-up daughters were much respected. Anyone
who was in the diplomatic service was very honoured. (One of
her daughters committed suicide.) So my poor parents, having
suffered bankruptcy, made my family a little inferior, though they
did not show it, but I could feel it.

My mother eventually found a flat in Zürich and collected me after two years to be with her. I went to school there and passed the equivalent of the English 11-plus, to my mother's delight. I only saw my father the day I travelled to Britain to learn English. He lived in a flat in Basel and had changed from a lively, happy man into a dejected aged person. I could hardly recognise him but then 15 years had gone by and he must have been in his early sixties, as I was the last child and baby of the family.

Here now in Britain bankruptcy is not unusual these days and certainly not debasing. From the media I gather some people or businesses go bankrupt and so hope to forgo their debts and later start another business under a different name. If this is not found out it can happen more than once. I experienced this with a double glazing firm. I was given a 10-year guarantee and when I found a fault and wanted them to come and correct it, the firm had gone 'bust'. I also had a damp wall treated which cost £1,000, with a 30-year guarantee. Being 86 at the time, this would bring me to 116. My friends had a good laugh over me saying I'd come back to check the wall.

Of course there are the more honest big businesses who lose everything, their big houses, yachts, etc. by compensating and honouring their staff's promised pension and redundancy pay.

Chapter 115

Mothers, Daughters and Sons

A mother gives birth, loves and cares for her baby, keeps it clean, fed and happy, and gets up in the night umpteen times to give comfort when its crying wakes her. She helps the toddler in his early tentative walking, reads nursery rhymes and later takes the little child back and forth to nursery school. It does not end there. The next thing is the school run, and so on and on till the child is in its late teens and might leave home. Even then the care goes on, a job for life, hopefully with the help of the father. But sadly there are many single mothers coping alone.

In my nursing days with Waltham Forest Borough Council I must have visited thousands of families in the 12 years. After infectious diseases I would fill my time with visiting the aged. And I saw at first hand four different kinds of daughters and sons.

1) The loving daughter who cares for an elderly sick mother all her life, forgoing her youth, a possible marriage with children and of course grandchildren to love her in her old age. There are often other members of this family, but they are not interested as long as this daughter is willing to do her duty. Here the family should care enough to get together and decide a fair way to divide the responsibility and care for their mother, each taking turns. It might mean a home eventually, but this should be discussed by the family and of course with the aged mother herself if she still has her mental faculties. It should be explained to her that now may be the time for a proper nursing home where the facilities to care for her are much better, provided by professionals with proper equipment to meet all nursing needs.

I know of just such a girl who spent her youthful life caring for an ailing mother. She is now a woman in her fifties. Due to her loving care, her mother lived to 81. The daughter was then on her own, life had passed her by. She did find a loving relationship but too late for motherhood. Her other relations all had families, little children now grown up and with their own little children who adored her as a great-aunty, but she had no children of her own and never experienced the joy of a little baby in her arms to bring up and treasure.

2) The loving daughter whose mother still lives in her own home, being helped by social services and the local authority. She visits often and gives help; she is supportive and there when needed. She does not mind rolling up her sleeves to help with menial tasks which are now beyond her mother's energy.

One of the old ladies that I visited had a daughter who lived 30 miles away, yet in spite of her and her husband having full-time jobs, they visited regularly every two weeks at the weekend. They put her house in order as necessary then took her out for the afternoon. They missed very few times when there were other important events for them to attend but this would always be explained by telephone. The daughter was happy feeling she cared and her mother was happy feeling cared for.

3) Then there is the daughter who doesn't care. Yes, I have met them. Their first consideration is having a boyfriend or husband and still having fun and going out. Mum is lucky to see them on birthdays or at some of the other festivities. When babies arrive, mother can babysit and help out as long as she is fit enough. When old age takes its toll a home is immediately on the agenda. 'You'll be all right, we'll visit you!' But when the mother is actually in the home, their visits, which were often at first, then dwindle down to once or twice a year. I worked in an old people's home once for a couple of months and saw this kind of daughter or son. While many of the other residents had visitors daily by their side, this mother was lucky to see her daughter or son and their spouses on festive days like Easter or birthdays. Christmas was out as they always went abroad, seeking the sun. And when they did visit they did not arrive in a modest loving way, but rather as though their importance by having come exceeded anybody else's visits. When their mother was first admitted and her house was cleared of all possessions, they put the money raised in their account and told her, 'We will keep it safe for you!', which they did, till she died; then they used it for themselves. Other residents in the same

situation were given a cheque book by their daughter/son so they could get little goodies and Christmas presents for their friends and relations when they wanted.

Chapter 116

The Sex Bit

The joy of it, the technology of it, and all the rest of it. It sells newspapers: stories of eminent men who can't keep their trousers on when a pretty young thing makes eyes at them, MPs caught red-handed. Even Presidents have not escaped the astounding, sometimes even amusing publicity, and the ordinary chap, married with children, bringing home the bacon dutifully each Friday, wonders at the folly of those mightier than himself.

Sexual attraction and love are two different things, but when the two get together a wonderful life follows. It is sexual attraction which so often dies, and when someone says, 'I don't love you any more', what it really means is that real, deep love was never there. Real, deep love never dies. The man who lives for his mates and likes being the debonair young charmer and Romeo changes colour when children with their responsibilities arrive. With excuses, he disappears more and more from the family scene till eventually he vanishes altogether, leaving the once dashing young girl, now a responsible mother, whom he claimed originally to love, to cope on her own, as though he had nothing to do with the arrival of the little ones.

On the district, in my nursing career, as I mentioned in Chapter 92, a woman suffering from multiple sclerosis, bedridden and needing nursing attention, was still loved by her husband. Sex was definitely out, but this man learned to cope with a celibate life as it was more important to love and care for his helpless mate.

One of my friends experienced the unhappiness of an absconding husband. She was left with two small children. She felt very low and even stopped caring for her own looks. It was then she met a man, when taking the children to school, who saw her distress and

272

fell in love with her, just as she was, a real, deep love, a caring love, a love and compassion for her and even her children. He married her in spite of her ready-made family; he was a real man. She rewarded him by giving him another two children, as well as devotion and love, and it was fascinating to see her blossom out again as an attractive and sexy person.

Very often the birth leaves a mother low in spirit and it is at this time that many men stray, thinking because sex is not as it was, that this is the end of that kind of relationship. You read time and again in 'true life ' magazines that the man claims he left because 'I'm a man and I have needs', with the accent on *I*. If he had only waited and controlled his urges till his mate recovered from the birth trauma and the early upheavals of a new baby, all would have been all right again in time to come. This is where the real men are separated from the boys and where real fathers show their colours.

There is nothing more lovely and inspiring than to see an old couple celebrating their golden wedding anniversary with all their sons and daughters, grandchildren and even great-grandchildren surrounding them. They have stayed together through thick and thin, rough and smooth and now reap their reward.

Chapter 117

Laughter, Merriment, Smiles and Embarrassing Moments

LAUGHTER

Laughter makes the heart merry. Laughter in court might be taken in one of two ways a) complimentary or b) derisory. A life without laughter is a sad life indeed. In the four years that I have visited Longford Court I have never heard any of the residents laugh. Could it be that they are aware of their disability and see life passing them by? Do they comprehend that they will never have a partner, a home called their own and even children? Or are they so completely living in a grey cloud they are unaware of anything around them?

MERRIMENT

Merriment, enjoyed festive days, holidays etc: I've not seen this either in the home, but not because staff don't try to brighten up their lives. These residents, apart from their routine working pattern during the week, are taken out in the evenings and weekends for rides and into town, to places of interest, pubs and ice-cream parlours. Robin tells me when a holiday is due in the home and where they will be going, so he does comprehend and look forward to these occasions.

SMILES

Smiles are another thing absent in severely autistic people. Robin used to smile at everybody but not since admitted into care. I often say to him, 'Smile, Robin', and he gives a forced smile with no heart behind it. The realisation that he is in a home for good has affected him and there is nothing I can do to alter it. This is every parent's sorrow when their beloved son or daughter has to be admitted into care as they themselves get old. The deep importance of a given smile cannot be measured. A timid person will open up to a freely given smile. A doctor's smile can be more therapeutic than a pill; whereas his serious look will indicate disaster to a nervous patient. A smiling boss gives encouragement to his staff and a smiling employee is well liked.

On a lighter note:

EMBARRASSING MOMENTS

TEA FOR THE VICAR. The vicar came to visit us. I got him a cup of tea in my best porcelain. Robin, who was sitting next to him, poked his finger into the vicar's tea and licked it. The vicar still drank it.

THE FREE MEAL. I went for a blood test at Prince Charles hospital and subsequently went to the hospital restaurant to have lunch. It was Christmas time and the hospital was providing a Christmas dinner for staff, which meant visitors had to queue on the no-Christmas-dinner side. The restaurant manager was there to see all was orderly. I got to the till with a luscious meal costing £3, opened my handbag for my purse and to my dismay found no purse, having left it at home. With a queue behind me all waiting to pay, I felt like sinking into the ground with all those people, medical staff and visitors, watching me, and wondered whether I should put all the chosen food back again. Then the manager, who must have seen my embarrassment, motioned to the girl at the till to let me pass and he even helped me carry the tray to an empty table. Did I enjoy my free meal? Sort of. I did send a cheque for £5 with an apology and a Christmas card the next day.

CHRISTMAS SHOPPING. We went Christmas shopping with my daughter, her husband and Robin in Cardiff. We parked the car in a multi-storey car park with large yellow signs over the entrance called 'national' something. I can't remember exactly but felt this would be easily found with its large yellow sign. We had a lovely time shopping and, loaded up with bags, were trying to return to our car, looking for the yellow sign above the entrance. Would you believe it, there were six such signed car parks. We went from one to the other trying to find our car. We strutted back and forth and back again. No luck. We could not find our car. Were there more yellow-sign car parks? Frustrated, we stopped looking and went to the police and reported our car as stolen! Were we the first in such dire circumstances? The police smiled and asked us did we remember any places around the car park? We did have a little inkling and the police took us to the right car park and there stood our car waiting for us.

THE BLUE RIBBON. I flew to Zurich in Switzerland, where my grandson was to pick me up. I took my suitcase, which I had marked with a blue ribbon so I could recognise it easily, from the luggage carousel and we drove to his home just over the border in Germany. When I came to unpack my suitcase, what did I find? Shaving gear, men's pyjamas, men's attire and Lynx after-shave. And what did the man whom I presumed had my suitcase find? Ladies' lingerie and Moon Mist perfume! He too had marked his case with a blue ribbon. My grandson phoned Zurich airport to inform them of our mistake. Yes, a gentleman had also phoned that he had picked up the wrong case, and said he was sorry. We duly returned the wrong one and picked up ours the next day. It meant my grandson had to drive across to Switzerland once more.

M4 DILEMMA. I was invited by a friend, Pam Tunley, for the weekend. We met at a garden centre we both knew and I was then to follow her in my car to her house as I had not been there before. All was well till we got to a roundabout, when another car slipped between us and I lost her. I got onto the M4 but saw her nowhere, and stopped on the shoulder, not knowing what to do. A police patrol came by, stopped and the policemen asked me why I was there. I told him I was lost following my friend. Luckily I had her address with me and was able to show him. 'Follow me,' he said, and I was escorted by the police to my friend's house, where she was worrying about having lost me. She worried even more when seeing the police, till I emerged from my car and the policemen's car turned and drove away, leaving me to explain.

CAT'S WHISKERS. I came home from shopping and Felix the cat was sitting waiting by my front door. I said, 'Hallo lovely. Want to come in?' A man's head popped up from behind my neighbour's wall where he was doing some work and said, 'Yes, if you want...'

LAUNDERED MONEY. I once washed a pair of jeans which had three pound notes in the pocket that I had failed to see till I hung them up, so I pegged each note next to the jeans, with our dog Prince tied for protection to the laundry post. The notes dried out nicely and with a bit of ironing looked like new.

A CHILD'S OPINION. My car was in dock and I took my granddaughter on a bus. 'Look Granny, hasn't that man got a red nose?' Embarrassed, I got off at the next stop and told her, 'If you see anything odd or funny don't tell me in front of the person, tell me later.' I then took her on the next bus to finish our journey when she piped up, 'Look at that lady, Granny. We'll talk about her later.' End of that bus journey.

Chapter 118

St Luke's Church

Christ Church, Merthyr Tydfil, is a well-attended Anglican church in Wales. The church elders and Canon Steve Morgan decided to open a new little church on the nearby Gellideg council estate (this is called church planting). This would be a sister church to Christ Church. To attract people initially they offered refreshments at 10.45 a.m. prior to the service at 11 a.m. There was orange juice and biscuits for the children, tea, coffee and buttered toast for adults. At first only a few children came to enjoy the orange juice and biscuits. Soon other children followed, so, undeterred, the church team adjusted the service to suit the children. The children were used to enacting Bible stories, which they loved, feeling importantly involved. For example, the Good Samaritan: a boy was made to lie on the ground pretending to be injured, giving real agonising moans, and two other boys would walk by, ignoring the now even louder moans (the boy really enjoyed moaning and groaning, a real actor in the making). Then the Good Samaritan would come and bandage his wounds with real bandages and put him on his horse (another boy's back) and take him to the inn. Each Sunday the team had prepared another story and the children just loved to take part. The girls were put in charge of the video screen and manipulated the changing of hymns, another important task. How they loved it! More children came and eventually some brought their parents. So the congregation began to grow. The Reverend John Parkin was himself a great performer, egging the children on enthusiastically. When parents started to come they loved to see their children performing and willingly took part in hymn singing. Far better for the children to sing hymns and enact Bible stories than hang around the streets being bored.

278

The children were taken to a camp holiday once or twice a year, paid for by the church and parishioners.

FAITH HEALING

Because of my autistic Robin, I went to many faith-healing sessions, which come to churches every once in a while. Of course these sessions were so crowded I never got a look-in for Robin, but I witnessed some extraordinary happenings. People were healed and people were prayed over by the ministers and fell down in a swoon. I, being sceptical, thought it was just a kind of hysterical exhibition. Years ago I fell off a horse and injured my back, which bothered me for years to come. It became particularly bad in the 1990s. Christ Church, which I attend, offers prayers to anyone in need in the side chapel after the service. I went and told them of my bad back, and two church elders prayed over me with hands on my head. A most peculiar feeling came over me and I must have fainted. I lay on the floor with the most wonderful feeling coming over me, and ever since then I have been sorry not to have stayed there longer to enjoy this calming heavenly feeling. As I got up, in that moment I was aware of my earthly surroundings. Two years later one of the elders who had prayed over me said to me, 'And how is your back?' Puzzled, I looked at him and said, 'What back?'

St Luke's Church's ministry team offer prayers regularly to those wishing it and I saw ordinary mothers who had only recently joined this little church being prayed over and having the same experience as I had. They fell down, yet they had never witnessed healing sessions before so they knew nothing about others falling down.

This little church is going places. It may not be overflowing with congregation but the team pray over the children each Sunday. Let's hope it will be a lasting foundation for them and help them into a responsible adult life.

MIRACLES

In one of the surgeries I attended was a notice on the board which read: 'the impossible we attempt, but miracles take a little longer'. Yes, I believe in miracles, they do exist.

Apart from my back trouble, which has completely left me, I

279

witnessed two more miracles. On each occasion I had a disabled person in my charge. I was doing voluntary work for Tarian (battered wives) and took a young woman with learning difficulties shopping. We parked in the college car park and when we returned with bags of food, found a car parked opposite me, not in a proper parking space. It was so near that I had difficulty manoeuvring my car out. I must have just touched the other car. All this time my charge stood there waiting with her shopping bags. A man came and said to me, 'I saw that.' 'All right,' I said. Then two ladies came whose car it was and started to accuse me. 'All right,' I said. 'I'll give you my insurance number and particulars.' At this moment a Panda car, which I had never before seen in this car park, appeared and a policewoman got out and said, 'This car is unlawfully parked,' took their address and number down and I was let off, so I took off for home with my charge.

Next, a friend of mine had serious disabling arthritis. Her disabled son (he had learning difficulties) was in a home. Once a year he could come home for a week and I would have him, to save his mother work she could no longer do. Robin was in St Tydfil's hospital at that time, between homes. The young man's name was Paul and he loved mountains and waterfalls. I took him to almost every waterfall around Merthyr. There was only one left we wanted to see, and we followed a group of walkers we thought were going to this waterfall. The path was high up and narrow. After about a mile I called out to the leader of the walking party, 'How much further is the waterfall?' 'Waterfall?' he said. 'What waterfall? We're not going to a waterfall,' and they went on. So there we were, a long way from where we had started, on a very small path up a small Welsh mountain. I looked down with horror. Whereas I was all right following the group, no way could I go back down this narrow path on my own, in charge of a disabled young man who trusted me completely, and fear gripped me. The walking group was now out of sight and we were alone. The reader may not believe me or think I was mad, but all of a sudden we were right at the bottom where we began and I could not believe my eyes. A miracle?

Chapter 119

The Mother-in-Law Dilemma

Having visited thousands of families in my work, the most frequent upset I found was the mother-in-law dilemma. She brought up a son, cared for him and now sees some of the mistakes the inexperienced wife makes. She dares point them out and there is havoc to pay.

In one family, a dispute of seven years escalated throughout the family from one single remark picked up by the daughter-in-law about a will. The daughter-in-law thought that her husband should be the beneficiary but she believed some other member of the family was to profit. The rift caused by this daughter and widowed mother-in-law was so great, even the grandchildren were not allowed to see their grandmother any more. Birthday presents sent by her were not acknowledged. She did try and make contact, several times. She even got through to her son on the telephone, who said, yes, he would come and talk about it. But that was as far as it got; he did not come. Was this after he had consulted his wife? They even avoided her when she had to go into hospital for an operation. Only neighbours and friends visited her. When eventually home, strangers living near brought her flowers and welcomed her back. Had this daughter-in-law faced her mother-in-law and asked outright about her suspicion, it could all have been resolved.

Then there is the case of the mother and daughter relationship gone sour. The daughter was in her forties, the mother in her seventies. The daughter never grew up and she thought it was still her mother's duty to support, shield and help her. All the past years her mother had been there when things went wrong in her marriage, even cared for her two little children for five years while the daughter went in and out of hospital with a depressive illness.

281

Now the daughter was married again and had her own house, while her mother was now ailing, living alone. The rift was caused by the mother daring to complain about the lack of help forthcoming. Instead of discussing the issue, the daughter completely ignored her mother's complaint and the animosity grew until they became like two strangers; love had died.

Initial diplomatic negotiations can resolve disputes and stop them in their tracks, whether they are family rift or even wars.

Old or widowed people still love to be respected. Sometimes a grandmother is just used for baby-sitting and knitting. Happy is the grandmother who is included in holiday plans, and happy are the grown-up children with toddlers who are part of the Christmas festivities where the parents take the burden rather than following the modem trend of flying abroad to have fun. Christmas is hard work if at home with all the children and the children's children together, but it has bonded many a shaky marriage or relationship and brought its own reward and satisfaction: a united family.

Chapter 120

The Voluntary Sector and Charities

A recent government report states that the voluntary workforce in Britain has saved the government at least one million pounds each year. There are hundreds of voluntary car drivers, some attached to the ambulance service, others to the different voluntary organisations. These drivers take patients back and forth to hospital appointments, leaving the ambulance service free to take the more serious cases. As I have mentioned, I did car voluntary service when in the Forest of Dean. This service was attached to the Social Services Department and catered for patients being taken to their different meetings and therapeutic social gatherings. In Cardigan Bay this service was attached to the ambulance service, who phoned me almost daily to give me the lighter cases to transport to and from hospital appointments.

There are hundreds of different voluntary organisations throughout the world.

THE RED CROSS, with its main seat in Geneva, Switzerland, is one of the largest voluntary organisations. It spreads its wings all over every continent. Wherever disaster strikes, The Red Cross will be there, giving whatever help is needed.

OXFAM has shops in every town and even in some villages, collecting clothes, blankets and money for needy countries.

AMNESTY INTERNATIONAL fights against cruelty and injustice.

CHURCHES collect for needy causes and countries abroad.

Then there are hundreds of voluntary services that serve the needs of this country.

TARIAN helps abused women and their children, providing safe shelter away from the offending partner/husband. I worked for battered wives for four years and it was an eye-opener to this nasty social scourge.

AGE CONCERN helps the aged and organises informative meetings, coffee mornings and socials.

RSVP (Retired Senior Volunteer Programme) has a network covering England, Wales, Scotland and Ireland. I was organiser for RSVP in Merthyr for five years and had 32 volunteers; multiply this by all other regions in the United Kingdom and it will give you an idea of the vast network of this organisation, which places its volunteers in numerous activities: voluntary car driving for hospitals, cancer care, reading in schools, visiting the housebound, etc.

Not to forget the numerous animal charities who care for animal welfare and fight against animal cruelty here and abroad. PDSA are top of the list: they make possible medical care for animals belonging to the not so well off.

And last but not least all the good people who care for their disabled or convalescent neighbours, providing help with shopping, taking meals and performing many other little caring actions.

Chapter 121

The Hugging Culture

The open unashamed hugging culture came in with royal approval with the late Diana, Princess of Wales. People hug on the football pitch, they hug on TV, in chat shows, competition shows, in *Come Dancing* and *Strictly Dancing*. Teenagers chasing fortune with stars in their eyes all hug each other now; they hug, lose or win. They hug if you win in joy, they hug if you lose in consolation. All a release of pent-up emotion. The hug is here to stay.

Of course the kiss on the cheek was already in Switzerland and France, not only one kiss but one on both cheeks, and has been quite customary abroad. Here, if I kissed my friends on both cheeks they would think I was mad. Eskimos, I understand, touch noses. The kiss too has become more popular; even presidents kiss and hug now quite openly. They hug friends, rivals, adoring fans – and sometimes a bit more, but that's another story.

When I came to Britain in 1937 the hug was something private. Imagine Winston Churchill hugging President Roosevelt or the dictator Stalin of Russia? The English were then known for their reserve (stiff upper lip), not showing their emotions, which I believe was a public school syndrome the working classes copied.

But not any more. Anything goes: green hair, rings in noses, lips and even bellybuttons, which are duly exposed to give them the expected honour. This is the liberated century. Marriage is shunned by many and there is homosexual freedom as never before.

Yet somehow this freedom has its darker side. Two elderly lonely ladies cannot share their lives in case they're labelled lesbians and similarly two bachelors sharing a flat together may be marked as gay. And a loving mother with a disabled grown-up son, taking him with her on holiday and everywhere else, loving him, protecting

285

him, might be labelled suspicious and even a hug given a sexual innuendo.

After my abuse accusations from the Carmarthen health team, I was afraid of even hugging Robin as this might further arouse these monstrous suspicions. So Robin is lucky to get a peck on the cheek whenever I visit or leave, yet when I take him to our church, the ladies there all give him a hug because he looks so much younger than his real age and of course his disability makes him even more endearing. This makes me feel sad that I cannot give him a cuddle when I'm really entitled to do so. The accusation is still deep in my heart and does not seem to go away, and I still feel there are some people who were involved who believe what they heard on the bush telegraph, the whisper which goes from ear to ear. After all, there is no smoke without fire, or so the saying goes.

Chapter 122

The Vulnerable

There is a section of people who are very vulnerable. They have no voice, they are on their own, having lost their partner or spouse young or old; and single mothers whose child's father either left or would not recognise his own. The saying 'Together we stand, divided we fall' comes into its own.

In my case, with the appalling accusation of abuse to my own son and all the other disrespectful treatment dished out, I often wonder if it would have been different had I had a man by my side. The answer would have to be yes. I had friends in Cardigan whose son had a mental illness and were under the same consultant as Robin. His parents thought their son might be gluten-sensitive, as suggested by the Schizophrenia Society's leaflets, exactly the same as I had claimed. They were allowed gluten-free bread on prescription. My request was ignored. And again when we moved to Merthyr, would the bush telegraph have had the same effect with a man by my side? I doubt it. They wouldn't have dared. The health team meetings where I was made a laughing stock, with a man by my side I would have been protected and treated with restraint.

At King's College hospital we nurses were told to treat with respect and courtesy all patients, whether they were nobles or dustmen or single and unprotected, and their visitors were to be treated like guests. Unfortunately this does not seem to be honoured in other parts of the health service and I think it is due to lack of training in this field.

Having visited hundreds of homes and families, I found respect, love and compassion lacking in many. A mother-in-law loses her husband and from that moment on she becomes a second-class citizen in the eyes of a daughter-in-law, and this can even happen with the real daughter. Old age means becoming a 'has-been'. And yet I found daughters and daughters-in-law being loving and kind, spending time helping an aged, now lonely and maybe ailing relative.

Nowadays the single mother may be lucky and have her parents' support. Her father may still protect her and let his voice be heard when problems arise, still caring for his daughter and for his little grandson/daughter. But when I was a district nurse 50 years ago, I found single girls barely out of their teens with nobody caring whether they lived or died, their parents having washed their hands of them, thinking about the shame on the family, a child out of wedlock, the good social services her only rock.

Chapter 123

Consultants Versus Consultants
(The Caring and the Not So Caring)

While I was in the Forest of Dean my relationship with Robin's consultants was good. I received help and advice whenever needed. Letters I sent were answered. Things changed drastically later when in Cardigan. The consultant in Carmarthen was less approachable and when I dared mention that the medication prescribed at that time upset Robin, hoping he might do something about it or explain to me how to cope, I got no answer (see Chapter 62). Years later when Robin was in Longford Court and I was still not satisfied with his medication (two different drugs had been added to the prescription recommended by Professor Robin Murray, prescribed by the consultant in Merthyr, where his requested additive-free diet was not honoured), I wrote to Professor Robin Murray asking him what dosages Robin was on when he left the Bethlehem hospital. I had a letter by return from the great man himself. Apart from the medication and dosage, he wrote: 'I hope things are going well with Robin, as I like to know what happens to my former patients. I would be grateful if you could drop me a line to let me know.' A very caring, professional man. I felt honoured.

In Carmarthen the psychiatric consultant did not answer Dr A.H. Hodson's letter re Robin's allergies (Chapter 62). And in Merthyr Tydfil I wrote to the consultant about my worries re medication:

On visits, which last up to four hours on a Sunday afternoon (playing Scrabble) and on home visits we have noticed Robin going to the toilet very frequently and he also keeps saying he feels sick and he walks around like a tiger in a cage. On other occasions he falls asleep and is completely unwakeable.

289

Robin was on Clozapine only and no other drug in the Bethlehem hospital under Professor Robin Murray for just over three months, and they had no behaviour problems, as they honoured my requested additive-free diet.

In the three private homes Robin had been placed prior to Longford Court, his diet was not adhered to and consequently his behaviour deteriorated. I notice now he is on Benperidol 0.75 mg *Mane* and 0.5 mg *Nocte*.

In my *Materia Medica*, Benperidol is stated to have following side effects: 'Sedation and pyramidal symptoms are likely to occur. There may be also restlessness ... gastrointestinal disturbances, difficulty in urinating.' Robin being on an additive-free diet now, I wish him to be taken off Benperidol as I believe his feeling sick and frequency in having to urinate, his restlessness and odd times of falling asleep are due to Benperidol. Robin is unable to tell this on consultation with you but tells me, his mum. Staff at Longford Court thought it prudent to get professional guidance as regards Robin's diet and having heard different views on the subject had him tested at an allergy clinic in Cardiff. And now it is established 'Robin is in need of an additive-free diet'! I realise that he can be taken off the requested extra medication and know it has to be done very slowly over a period of time... Yours. etc.

This letter was sent 19th January 2005 and I have not had an answer as yet. Robin is still on these two extra drugs and my worries remain.

At the last progress meeting for Robin, the consultant mentioned that he wished to pass Robin's care to another doctor. I was given to understand by Mr Anthony Jeffers, the manager of Longford Court, that this was difficult because Robin had been sectioned. This was news to me. He went into Abergavenny as a voluntary resident, then into Bethlehem hospital again voluntarily. He went into Thomastown House, again voluntarily. Where did the sectioning happen and why? Which exact section was he admitted under and at what date? Why was I not informed when and how it happened? I have never received any such news in writing. No doubt all the problems making sectioning necessary were due to his additive allergies which were ignored.

Chapter 124

Confidentially Speaking?

A wise old owl sat on a rock
The more he saw the less he spoke
The less he spoke the more he heard
Why aren't we all like that wise old bird
(Richards)

Discretion shall preserve thee... The words of a tale bearer are as wounds, and they go down into the innermost parts of the belly. Death and life are in the power of the tongue (Proverbs)

Unfortunately, people love to hear about the misfortunes to others. There was the newspaper street vendor who called out again and again, 'Ain't it awful!' He sold twice as many newspapers as the other vendor on the opposite side of the street, who stood just quietly selling his papers. Everyone wanted to know what was awful.

When I did my training for district nursing, the matron in charge told us more than once the importance of confidentiality, never ever tell family A what family B were doing or even what illnesses they had; there was nothing worse than a nurse going from house to house gossiping about matters which were confidential. The harm that can be caused by revealing what goes on behind closed doors can be devastating. This of course applies also to hospitalised patients and those in nursing homes and institutions. One should be able to trust nurses and doctors with the innermost secrets.

Gossip, including by telephone, has had some serious consequences, making people unhappy and even progressing to court cases.

Malicious gossip has ruined many people's reputation and is one of the hardest to undo.

A man unjustly labelled as a child molester by false gossip – a case of mistaken identity – could not prove himself innocent and had eventually to leave the area.

A woman was accused of infidelity when a prying neighbour saw the same man, not her husband, several times leaving her house (he was a salesman). This story got round the district and was hard to explain as innocent. It stuck till the husband, annoyed, threatened to consult a solicitor.

This brings me back once again to my own unhappy state and Robin's with regard to his diet, the past accusations and the bush telegraph. Had confidentiality been observed when I moved to Merthyr, I would have had a new start in 'fresh fields', in other words.

Chapter 125

The Wonder of Electricity and Computers

Chambers Dictionary: '**electricity** ... the manifestation of a form of energy associated with separation or movement of charged particles, such as electrons and protons; the science that deals with this ... an electric charge or current'.

This is another of the natural power wonders besides water and fire. You can store it in batteries and it can be used at your convenience. You can't see it except when lightning occurs and you can observe its frightening power, feeling: beware, it can kill you. Many people have been killed by lightning when in an open field during a thunderstorm, and equally many have been killed by faulty electrical items, not to mention houses burnt down due to an electrical fault. So beware, treat electricity with respect and let an approved electrician check your appliances regularly.

Imagine when this power was first recognised – I cannot say invented, because it was there all the time, waiting to be found. Imagine when New York switched on the electric lights in all their streets for the first time, the wonder and the parties that followed this great event. Now we take it all for granted, we switch on the lights whenever we like and pay the bill.

I look around my house: there must be at least 20 different electrical appliances I take for granted, including larger items like the cooker and 'hover' lawnmower, and smaller things like food blenders, hairdryers etc.

Computers

This amazing small machine, impossible without electricity, can record thousands of documents and store them in its memory. I understand it can open up the world and bring thousands of advertised bargains into your home, including the best bargains in flights abroad and other such important matters. You might even find love through a computer. And if a bug does get introduced into it, you tear your hair out and so will thousands of other computer users. Beware, it can corrupt your children if not monitored, and land you in jail if illegal or pornographic material is found. Yet as recorded in my first chapter, the quadriplegic Rick Hoyt, who was thought to be a complete vegetable, progressed on a computer, not only to communicate. He started to learn from scratch; and even attended university and took a degree, finishing up as a computer scientist at Boston University.

I understand that Robin is being entered by Longford Court into the South West Wales Open College Network for five programmes, including how to use a computer, and is beginning to learn how to understand it. The possibility is that he'll know more eventually about computers than I do.

I have a laptop I use only for writing and printing at the moment. To my frustration I find children know more about computers than I do. Many times have I rushed out and grabbed teenage schoolboys from the street, asking them into my house to help where my understanding had failed me, and they were able to assist me when the computer went wrong, or I misused it. What error did I make? As for my helpful neighbours Tony and Steven, I would be totally lost without them. This little machine is so sensitive I have to watch not to touch anything except the actual letters in the document. Many times I have touched something which either wiped off all I had written or, stranger still, circles or squares appeared that I could not eliminate by myself.

So without electricity we would be back in the Dark Ages.

Chapter 126

Friends, Relations and Robin's Weekly Activities at Longford Court

The importance of family involvement with a disabled person can never be measured. A caring brother, sister or any relative spending time with a disabled person regularly, apart from giving happiness, also has its own reward of the feeling of satisfaction. Often the success a disabled person reaches is due to the love and care of the family or even just one family member. In Robin's case, my weekly visits not only give me a feeling of happiness but Robin looks forward to my coming and would have me stay much longer than the four hours I usual spend with him. And every parting is with a little regret and sorrow at having to leave him behind and not being able to have him home. It brings to my mind the book I read by Pearl Buck years ago. She had a disabled child and felt it was unfair for the rest of the family to care for its extensive nursing needs. She describes the inner battle she had when deciding to place this child in a home for disabled children, and goes on to explain when she first brought this child to the home and left it behind, she could hear the child crying out after her, calling, crying, on and on; 'Mummy … mummy…' It nearly rent her heart.

Robin is not a child but, as mentioned before, I think he is a child in a man's body due to his disability and I still wish he could be normal, independent and free of spirit. And although Longford Court is the right place for him to be, he still would prefer to be at home. He does not call out in distress, 'Mum … mum…' But he calls out repeatedly, 'See you next Sunday … see you next Sunday', and I confirm his request till I'm out of earshot.

Robin's weekly activities (as reported to me):

295

Robin attends Glamorgan House on a weekly basis doing pottery classes Mondays and Wednesdays from 1.30–2.30 p.m., arts and crafts lessons Thursdays 1.30–2.3 p.m. In-house activities include a night out on Mondays for two to three hours and a minibus journey to Knoll Neath Nature park for a walk around between 10 a.m. and 12 p.m. Tuesdays and Thursdays, out for lunch and a drive. Friday, a day out to Margam Park for gardening and a walk about 9 a.m.–12. Wednesdays and Saturdays, usually a spin in the minibus to enjoy scenery and trips. Sundays, weather permitting, there are picnics with the other residents somewhere nice. If he is in the right mood there is the opportunity to race round on the go karts that are provided in Longford Court grounds. Robin is also taken out to do shopping, to choose his own clothing and at Tesco some of his own food, and he pays for these things himself to teach him to handle money.

Chapter 127

Mental Illness/Schizophrenia

There is nowt so odd as folk, or as the Cornish farmer said to his wife, 'The whole world be mad 'cept thee and me and thee is a bit peculiar'.

Schizophrenia covers a multitude of different conditions. I wonder who coined this fear-inspiring name, and when – a name which makes people recoil, and those who have been labelled so, and their relatives hide in shame. This name certainly is not mentioned in the Bible.

Instead of using this umbrella term, it would be so much more humane to name the particular branch of mental illness, e.g. mental stress, depressive illness, paranoid, neurosis, self-harm, suicidal tendencies, mania, etc. Only very few lead to murder. If you compare the few numbers of violent acts perpetrated by the mentally ill in comparison with the high number of murders committed by the so-called normal population, the mentally ill are in the minority. A mentally ill patient is on the whole an unaggressive person, yet there is a commotion when one mentally ill patient becomes dangerous. Then the cry of the multitude is 'Lock them all up'. Hundreds of people labelled schizophrenic are under treatment, unknown to their neighbours, and lead normal lives; some are even employed, earning a living.

The way I understand it from reading leaflets given out by the Schizophrenia Association of Great Britain is that there is a substance called dopamine (a chemical found in brain tissue that acts as a neurotransmitter necessary for the normal functioning of the brain). Too much dopamine causes mental disturbances, too little causes Parkinson's disease (shaking hands etc.). So much medication prescribed for metal illness to block dopamine can cause side effects like shaking hands (see also Chapter 69).

Generally the highest incidence of schizophrenia was reported in wheat- or rye-eating areas of the world, then, in descending order of incidence, oats, rice, sorghum and millet.

Of the 6,313 million people worldwide, 1 per cent suffer from schizophrenia. In the UK out of 58,789,194 population half a million are so affected.

I should know all about this nasty illness, as two of my children were diagnosed schizophrenic when reaching the age of 15 years. Their childhood seemed normal. They all went to Sunday school, were fetched to and from school until 10 years old, joined Brownies, Girl Guides, Cubs and Scouts. They all enjoyed going to camp and had birthday parties where their friends were invited yearly, and the girls were allowed to bring their boyfriends home when in their teens. I honoured their school do's and always attended. I loved them all. So what went wrong? I became a single parent when the youngest was still only five years old and the eldest fourteen, but so did many other mothers. I blame it on the Second World War. My husband came out of it a very restless man. Because of this illness in my family I attended parent meetings with other affected families, and found the majority ordinary loving parents, completely bewildered by this illness of their daughter/son.

Reported recently in the national press:

Echoes of Vietnam: more than a quarter of American soldiers who seek hospital treatment after returning from Iraq and Afghanistan are suffering from metal disorder. Post-traumatic stress disorder is the most common diagnosis of former troops being treated in veterans' hospitals over the past 16 months, and the number of patients is expected to rise. Around 20 per cent of all eligible former soldiers visited the hospitals between October 2003 and February 2005, and 26 per cent of those were diagnosed with the disorder, according to the *New England Journal of Medicine*. About 31 per cent of male soldiers who served in Vietnam developed the condition.

After the Falklands War, men from the armed forces sued the Government for abnormalities passed on in their genes to their offspring due to the injections they had been given against illness and gas warfare. In the Second World War, the armed forces too were given all kinds of injections, especially when serving abroad.

298

My husband was in Aden and he too was subject to numerous poisonous injections against tropical diseases, gas warfare etc. He caught tropical sores and malaria (which recurred many years after discharge). He was discharged a year before the war ended, like many others who suffered from shellshock, post-traumatic shock, neuroses, etc.

I did an extra-mural four-year University of London Social Science course in the 1970s. Psychological Aspects was the last subject, for which I read Freud, Adler and Jung. It became quite obvious that mental illness seemed to be blamed on the mothers. I don't remember the war being mentioned. As for damaged genes and them being passed on to offspring, this was not yet recognised.

I myself was turned inside out and outside in by eager social workers trying to establish the cause of my children's mental illness. They obviously suspected me, the mother. None of these social workers, some so young they had only just passed out of training, had experienced war nor seemed to know of its after effects, or the possibility of inheriting damaged genes. I too was in London during the war and experienced the nightly sirens and the bombing. By the grace of God I never had to have psychiatric treatment and worked as a nurse throughout those devastating times.

The happy final ending is, my grandchildren are all right and the illness has not been passed down to them.

Conclusion

Robin was partly autistic from the day he was born (1956). Autism at that time does not seem to have been recognised. He seemed quite happy as long as he was not pressurised, and was able to tag along in infant school and other activities. I helped him at home by reading to him all the little books which teach the alphabet. It was not till much later I realised, although he could read, he did not actually take all of the contents in, not the more advanced stories anyway. Again at home I spent many hours doing sums with him. Consequently he became very good at arithmetic and still is. Robin is rather like a computer, taking in and giving out information. This is shown by the way he plays and wins at Scrabble, a game which we played often at home.

It was when he got to senior school that his limitations came to the fore and when the boys started to bully him he became disturbed. This is when I took him to see a professor at the London hospital psychiatric unit. He was diagnosed as having schizophrenia, the symptoms and commencement at 15 suggested this. Of course in Robin's case it was due to being pressurised for the first time in his life and bullied by other boys. Because the diagnosis was schizophrenia I spent the next 30 years hoping for a cure which might exist for schizophrenia, but not autism.

As any other mother, I would grab at any straw which promised to help, including visiting what I thought was a nature therapist, as advertised in yellow pages, but who was in fact a sex therapist. Was this part of the wrongful accusations I received in Carmarthen (of abuse?), this being told to my doctor and it being misconstrued. Surely not!!

When Robin was discharged from the London hospital he was

much worse. He had escalated to 14 stone and was like a zombie. This must have been the drugs he was put on. At home I got his weight down to his normal 10 stone and as reported in an earlier chapter found Robin to react aggressively to food additives. By monitoring his food he became his old confused self and was manageable.

There followed happy years in the Forest of Dean, then more happy years in Llechryd, Dyfed, near Cardigan. I registered him with the local art club, took him swimming, went riding with the disabled, went to a social club one evening a week where he played snooker and table tennis and we also joined the local badminton club. He went to Newcastle Emlyn occupational therapy unit during the week and took his additive-free food with him. This worked very well till someone at Newcastle Emlyn thought it was wrong for Robin to have different food from the other clients and my nightmare began. How did they deal with other special diets like diabetes etc? He was admitted under a forced section from the occupational therapy unit for aggression the first time; I had already had disagreements over his medication regarding some of the nasty side effects but received no real help or explanation to improve same. This is where things started to go drastically wrong, which is explained in some of the chapters of this book. Apart from the main accusation of abuse I was also accused of withholding his medication when he was home on weekend leave. I am a highly trained ex-nurse (King's College hospital, London), no way would I withhold medication knowing it would be given again when back in hospital, playing a yo-yo game with my own son's life.

With all those things going wrong, I wonder who is in charge in some of the mental hospitals, the consultant or the staff? Who makes vital decisions and accusations, ridiculing a mother's findings, assessing a mother's character etc? And I would have thought assessing a mother's character to be a consultant's role, including getting her trust and being able to communicate harmoniously without the feeling the consultant was God; also keeping staff informed in a human way. Very serious allegations should be discussed with the senior consultant and monitored and if found to be based on suspicion only, quashed by him.

I moved to Merthyr Tydfil for a clean start with hopefully helpful social workers. It was fine at first till the bush telegraph from Carmarthen got cracking, no doubt feeling resentful about a 'nearly' court case and having had to give me a letter of apology admitting their wrong. Telephone conversations from borough to borough may be helpful, or otherwise, for a newly moved in resident, provided the staff treat this professionally and confidentially. Readers can draw their own opinions from some of the chapters dealing with this part. Everything stopped for Robin, art, riding, playing badminton etc., when in Merthyr.

Luckily after three very badly run homes where his requested diet was ignored, with consequent aggression, resulting in further section admissions to hospital, Robin is now in Longford Court for autistic people, an extremely well-run home, where there is plenty of occupational therapy and an almost normal working day pattern, doing gardening, pottery, art, etc., and most important of all his requested diet is honoured. He went into this home with the burden of dyskinesia (*Chambers* dictionary: 'lack of control over bodily movement, impaired performance of voluntary movement'). He picks up items or non-existing things, which he did not do prior to going into care. Dyskinesia is a condition due to medication, and I blame the over-medication Robin received while in the Abergavenny nursing home because the requested additive-free diet was not honoured and this caused Robin's disturbances. The medication being:

Loxapine 100 mg once daily (not listed in my *Materia Medica*).

Procyclidine 5 mg twice daily (*Bloomsbury's Materia Medica*: 'a powerful anticholinergic drug used to relieve symptoms of Parkinson's, specifically the tremor of the hands, the overall rigidity of the posture, and the tendency to produce an excess of saliva. (The drug also has the capacity to treat these conditions in some cases where they are produced by drugs.) Side effects are dry mouth, dizziness, blurred vision and gastrointestinal disturbances. Maybe, in sensitive patients, confusion, agitation and psychological disturbance.')

Largactil 100 mg three times daily (*Bloomsbury's Materia Medica*: 'a powerful preparation of the powerful Phenothiazine drug Chlorpromazine hydrochloride, a major tranquillizer, an anti psychotic... Side effects: concentration, thought and movement are affected, dry mouth, blocked nose, difficulty in urinating and blurred vision.')

302

Flupenthixol (cone) 100 mg twice weekly as required (PRN) (*Bloomsbury's Materia Medica*: 'a powerful antidepressant drug; side effects: insomnia and restlessness. Should be administered with extreme caution, heart, kidneys and liver at risk.')

Droperidol 40 mg. Up to twice daily (BD) (*Bloomsbury's Materia Medica*: 'Tranquillizer and anti-psychotic for manic patients ... side effects: restlessness, insomnia, nightmares, rashes, dry mouth, gastrointestinal disturbances, difficulty in urinating and blurred vision.')

Temazepam nocte (*Bloomsbury's Materia Medica*: 'a relatively short acting hypnotic drug, one of the benzodiazepines, used as a tranquillizer to treat insomnia and as an anxiolytic pre-medication prior to surgery. Side effects: concentration and speed of reaction are affected, drowsiness and dizziness may occur. Prolonged use may result in tolerance and finally dependence.')

This is when I took him to the Bethlehem hospital under Professor Robin Murray, where they took him off all drugs and replaced them with only one, Clozapine (different from Loxapine). It didn't take long for Robin to be put back on several drugs again when back in Merthyr as again his requested diet was not honoured.

So Longford Court received Robin not the way he had been cared for at home but a Robin adulterated medically with dyskinesia, constantly feeling unwell due to side effects, and of course due to his frustrations there were incidents, though the home did not complain but dealt with them in a dignified way. Where does that leave Robin and me? I worry constantly as I feel we are in the consultant's hands, and he does not seem to care. Robin feels no one believes him and frustration takes over and the home has no power or knowledge to alter his medication.

Helpful Charities, Associations and Societies

Abuse

1) NSPCC Child Protection Helpline for people who are concerned about children and young people at risk of abuse, including calls from children and young people themselves. Offers information, advice and counselling about the welfare of children. Tel. 0808 800 5000. (24 hours) www.nspcc.org.uk

2) Family Matters provides counselling and support for survivors: adults and children over eight. Tel. 01474 537392. (24 hours)

3) Support line for young children, young adults at risk and victims of abuse: Tel. 0208 554 9004. www.supportline.org.uk

4) Pathways telephone support for adults and children who have experienced rape and/or sexual abuse, and children suffering any trauma. Also their friends, families and partners. Tel. 01685 379310

5) Stop it Now! An alliance of charities providing information and support. Tel. 0808 100 0900. www.stopitnow.org.uk

Age

1) Age Concern aims to promote the well-being of older people and make life fulfilling and enjoyable. Offers advice and support. Tel. 0800 009 966. www.ace.org.uk

2) Elder abuse response line provides a confidential information and support service for anyone concerned about abuse of an older person. Tel. 0808 808 8141. www.elderabuse.org.uk

3) Senior Line provides advice on welfare and disability benefits, community and residential care, housing options and adaptations, access to health and community services. Tel. 0808 800 6565. www.helptheaged.org.uk

Aids/HIV

1) National Aids Trust (NAT) works for policies that will prevent HIV transmission, improve access to treatment, challenge HIV stigma and discrimination and secure the political leadership to effectively fight Aids. Tel. 0207 814 6767. www.nat.org.uk

2) National Aids helpline provides advice and information about HIV, Aids and sexual health/local services. Calls to the helpline are confidential. Tel. 0800 567 123. Text phone: 0800 521 1361

Alcohol abuse

1) National Alcoholics Anonymous. Tel. 0845 769 7555. www.alcoholics-anonymous.org.uk

2) National Association for Children of Alcoholics (NACOA). Tel. 0800 358 3456. www.nacoa.org.uk

3) Al-Anon. Tel. 0207 403 0888. email alanonuk@aol.com www.al-anonuk.org.uk/alateen

Allergies

1) British Allergy Foundation offers information and support by a special nurse for people with allergies and their carers, the general public and health professionals. Tel. 0208 303 8583 (9 am to 9 pm Mon–Fri). www.allergyuk.org

Alzheimer's Disease

1) Alzheimer's Society. Tel. 0845 300 0336 (8.30 am to 6.30 pm Mon–Fri). www.alzheimers.org.uk

2) The Brace Appeal office, Blackberry Hill Hospital, Manor Road, Fishponds, Bristol, BS16 2EW. Tel. 0117 975 4831

3) Alzheimer's Research Trust, G.J. Livanos House, Granthams Road, Great Shelford. Tel. 01223 843 899. www.alzheimers-research.org.uk

Anorexia/Bulimia

Eating Disorders Association (EDA) provides information, help and support with a range of self services including telephone helplines, self-help network and membership. Adult helpline Tel. 0845 634 1414. Youth helpline (up to age 18) Tel. 0845 634 7650. www.edauk.com

Arthritis

1) Arthritis Research Campaign. Freepost 177, Chesterfield, S41 7TD. Tel. 0870 850 5000. www.arc.org.uk

2) The Source, a helpline for young people under 26 living with arthritis. Tel. 0808 808 2000

3) Arthritis Care helpline for confidential support backed up by useful publications. Everyone on the team has arthritis, you can talk confidentially to someone who understands. Aims to empower people to take control of their arthritis and their lives. Tel. 0808 800 4050. www.arthritiscare.org.uk

Asthma

1) AAIR (Asthma, Allergy & Inflammation Research), Centre Block, Southampton General Hospital, Tremona Road, Hants, S016 6YD. Tel. 0238 077 1234. www.aaircharity.org

2) Asthma UK, Adviceline 08457 010203. General 0207 786 5000. www.asthma.org.uk

Autism

1) National Autistic Society gives information and advice about autism and Asperger's syndrome for parents, friends and relatives or people with autism and Asperger's syndrome. Tel. 0870 600 8585. email autismhelpline@nas.org.uk www.nas.org.uk

2. Allergy-induced Autism, Rosemary Keswick Tel. 01733 833 1771.

Bankruptcy

1) The Insolvency Service provides initial information on insolvency legislation and procedures, including details of the work of the official receiver and what to expect. Tel. 0207 291 6895. www.insolvency.gov.uk

2) National Debt line offers free confidential information and advice on debt, including bank, credit card, finance, house mortgage arrears, council tax, catalogues, hire purchase and utility debts, issues dealt with include county court, refusal of credit, benefits, bankruptcy, harassment, housing, homelessness and bailiffs. Provides self-help information packs and a range of fact sheets. Tel. 0808 808 4000. www.nationaldebtline.co.uk

3) Business Debt line: self-help advice on debt problems for self-employed people and microbusinessess. Also provision of information packs and other self-help materials as appropriate. Service is free, confidential and independent. Tel. 0800 197 6026. www.bdl.org.uk

Battered wives

1) South Wales police domestic violence unit Merthyr 01685 724260, Rhonda Cynon Taff 01443 743679

2) Victim Support: Tel. 0845 303 0900. www.victimsupport.org.uk

Blind

1) National Blind Children's Society provides support for blind and visually impaired children. Tel. 0800 279 1555. email enquiries@nbcs.org.uk

2) Royal National Institute for the Blind (RNIB) offers practical support and advice to anyone with sight problems. Tel. 0845 766 9999. www.rnib.org.uk

Brittle bone disease

1) Brittle Bone Society gives advice, support and help to people with brittle bones (ontogenesis imperfecta) and promotes research into causes, inheritance and treatment. Tel. 0800 028 2459. www.brittlebone.org.uk

Broken relationships (marriage etc.)

1) Relate Central Office, Herbert Gray College, Little Church Street, Rugby, Warwickshire, CV21 3AP. Tel. 0845 456 1310 or 01788 573241

Bullying

1) Anti-bullying Campaign, 101 Borough High Street, London, gives support and advice. Tel. 0207 378 1446. email antibullying@compuserve.com

2) Parentline Plus helpline for anyone in a parental role including step parents and adoptive parents. Offers support and information on all issues of concern including education, bullying, alcohol and drugs, stealing and lying, sexual abuse and behaviour. Tel. 0808 800 2222

Cancer

1) Beating Bowel Cancer. Tel. 0208 892 5256. email info@beatingbowelcancer.org.uk. www.beatingbowelcancer.org.uk

2) Cancer BACUP nurses will answer any aspect of cancer, treatments etc. Tel. 0808 800 1234. www.cancerbacup.org.uk

3) Cancer Research UK, the largest volunteer supported cancer research into causes, prevention and treatment. Information on cancer, living with cancer, how to reduce your risk of cancer. Tel. 0207 242 0200

4) Cancer Care Bristol cancer help service, Grove House, Corn Wallis Grove, Bristol BS8 4PG. Tel. 01179 809513

5) Tenovus Cancer Charity, 43 The Parade, Cardiff, CF24 3AB. Tel. 0292 048 2000. email@tenovus.com. www.tenovus.com Tenovus freephone cancer helpline. Tel. 0808 808 1010

6) Macmillan Cancer Relief provides specialist nursing help. Tel. 0808 808 2020. www.macmillan.org.uk

Cardiac/heart

1) Cardiac Risk in Young (CRY). Emphasises the considerable amount that can be done to help young people who have been diagnosed as having cardiac condition. Counselling and support to families affected. Tel. 01737 363222 www.c-r-y.org.uk

2) Children's Heart Federation helpline for families and professionals involved with children with heart disorders. Information on all aspects of bringing up children with heart problems. Tel. 0808 808 5000. www.childrens-heart-fed-org.uk

3) British Heart Foundation publishes a range of excellent leaflets on various aspects of heart disease. Comprehensive website has a Healthy Heart section describing links between heart disease and smoking, alcohol, exercise, diet stress and high blood pressure. Tel. 0845 070 8070. www.bhf.org.uk

4) Cardiomyopathy Association. Telephone service for people with cardiomyopathy disease of the heart muscle, their families and professionals, information and support for the four separate conditions – hypertrophy, dilated, restrictive and arrhythmogenic right ventricular cardiomyopathies. Tel. 01923 249977. Freephone 0800 018 1024. www.cardiomyopathy.org

Carers

1) Carers UK is a campaign organisation which provides information and advice on all aspects of caring to both carers and professionals. Free phone line staffed by welfare rights, community care and benefits advisers. Tel. 0207 490 8818. www.carersuk.org

2) Carers line gives advice and information to carers, people who look after family, friends, partners, in need of help because they are ill, frail or have a disability. Advice on welfare, benefits, assessments and all community care issues. Tel. 0808 808 7777

3) Crossroads is the largest charity in the world providing 'in the home care' for carers. Tel. 0845 450 0350. www.crossroads.org.uk

4) Princess Royal Trust for Carers provides access to support, information and practical help to carers. There is a national network of over 100 independently managed Carers Centres across the UK. Tel. 0207 480 7788

Coeliac disease

1) Coeliac Association, PO Box 220, High Wycombe, Buckingham-shire. Tel. 01494 437278

2) Coeliac UK supports people with gluten intolerance, includes publications and helpline. Tel. 0870 444 8804. www.coeliac.co.uk

Cot death

1) The Child Death Helpline: professionals and parents working in partnership provide a listening service that offers emotional support to all those suffering by the death of a child. The helpline is staffed by bereaved parent volunteers. Tel. 0800 282 086. www.childdeathhelpline.org.uk

Cystic fibrosis

1) Cystic Fibrosis Trust, 11 London Road, Bromley, Kent, BR1 1BY. Tel. 0208 464 7211

Deafness

1) The Royal National Institute of the Deaf. Tel. 0808 808 0123 or 0808 808 9000. www.rnid.org.uk

2) The RNID Tinnitus helpline. 0808 808 666. Text phone 0808 808 0007

3) British Tinnitus Society: www.tinitus.org.uk

4) The Mennieres Association: www.mennieres.org.uk

5) The National Deaf Children's Society: Tel. 0808 800 8880. www.ndcs.org.uk

Debts

1) Debtaid offers free impartial advice and solutions for people who are in debt and wish to restart their lives afresh. Free information pack available. Tel. 0800 072 2332 www.debt.aid.ltd.uk

2) The UK Insolvency helpline is a national telephone helpline for people with debt problems. The service is free, confidential and independent. Expert advice and debt help information given over the phone. Tel. 0800 074 6918

Depression

1) Depression Alliance, 35 Westminster Bridge Road, London, SE1 7JB. Tel. 0845 123 2320. www.depressionalliance.org

2) Depressives Anonymous (self-help), Box FDA, 32–36 Pelham Road, Nottingham, NG1 2EG. Tel. 0870 774 4320. www.depressionanon.co.uk

3) Depression Alliance Cymru, 11 Plas Melin, Westbourne Road, Whitchurch, Cardiff, offers information and support to all those affected by depression. Tel. 02920 692891

4) Samaritans: Tel. 08457 90 90 90. email jo@samaritans.org. www.samaritans.org.uk

Diabetes

1) Diabetes UK: a leading charity working for people with diabetes, fund research, campaign and help people to live with the condition. Careline. Tel. 0845 120 2960. wwwdiabetes.org.uk

Down's syndrome

1) Downs Syndrome Association helps people with Down's syndrome

to live full and rewarding lives. Provides information, counselling and support for people with Down's syndrome, their families/ carers, as well as being a resource for professionals. Tel. 0208 682 4001. www. downs-syndrome.org.uk

Drug addiction

1) Drugscope provides quality drug information, promotes effective responses to drug taking, undertakes research at local, national and international levels and encourages informed debate. Tel. 0207 928 1211. www.drugscope.org.uk

2) Adfam: national helpline for families and friends of drug users. Offers information about drugs and details of local support and counselling for the caller's own concerns, family/relationships and anything related to the drug situation. Tel. 0207 289 8900. www.adfam.org.uk

3) Narcotics Anonymous: international community-based association of recovering drug addicts. Services are organised at local and international levels. Tel. 0207 730 0009. www.ukna.org.uku

4) Families Anonymous: for families of drug abusers, a self-help fellowship based on a 12-step programme. Aims to help the family and friends of people with current, suspected or former drug problems by providing mutual support. Tel. 0845 1200 660. www.famanon.org.uk

5) Battle Against Tranquillisers (BAT): helpline for people who wish to withdraw from tranquillisers or sleeping pills. Gives support for carers and runs groups at Bristol General hospital and Gloucester House, Southmead hospital. Tel. 01179 663629 www.bataid.org

6) Cocaine Anonymous (CA) is concerned solely with the personal recovery and continued sobriety of individual drug addicts who turn to them for help. Tel. 0207 284 1123. www.cauk.org.uk

Dyslexia

1) British Dyslexia Association gives help, support and advice. Tel. 01189 668271. www.bda-dyslexia.org.uk

Epilepsy

1) Cymru/epilepsi helps people with epilepsy in Wales to live as normal, active and productive a life in the community as possible. Gives support, advice or information. Tel. 0845 741 3774

2) The British Epilepsy Association gives information, advice and listening support for anyone with epilepsy or those with an interest in the subject. Advice and information on medical care, diagnosis, drugs, surgery, specialist services, education and employment. Tel. 0808 800 5050. www.epilepsy.org.uk

3) Epilepsy Research Foundation provides support, literature and information to people living with epilepsy. The ERF promotes and supports basic and scientific research into epilepsy. Tel. 0208 995 4781. www.erf.org.uk

Gambling

1) Gamcare provides advice, information and counselling for people affected by a gambling dependency and produces literature on gambling and related issues. Tel. 0845 600 0133. www.gamcare.org.uk

2) Gamblers Anonymous gives advice for anyone affected directly or indirectly. Tel. 0207 384 3040. www.gamblersanonymous.org

Haemophilia

1) Haemophilia Society provides information, advice and support services relevant to people with haemophilia, von Willebrand's and related disorders, advocates and campaigns to secure the best possible care and treatment. Tel. 0800 018 6068. www.haemophilia.org.uk

Homelessness

1) Crisis: national charity for solitary homeless people working to help vulnerable people get through the crisis of homelessness, fulfil their potential and transform their lives. Tel. 0870 011 3335. www.crisis.org.uk

Infertility

1) Inferility Network UK, Charter House, 43 St Leonards Road, Bexhill on Sea, TN40 1JA. Offers advice, information, support and a listening ear. Produces a range of fact sheets. Tel. 08701 188088. www.infertilitynetworkuk.com

Leukaemia

1) Leukaemia Care Society gives information, advice, counselling and befriending via network of volunteers for leukaemia sufferers, family and friends. Also financial support, summer holiday programme. Tel. 0800 169 6680. www.leukaemiacare.org.uk

Mad cow disease

1) National CJD Coordinator, Birchwood, Heath Top, Ashley Health, Market Drayton, Salop, TF9 4QR. Tel. 01630 673993. 106703.141@compuserve.com

Marriage care

1) Marriage Care helpline offers information, listening and counselling for those with marriage or relationship difficulties, and for those preparing for marriage. Tel. 0845 660 6000. www.marriagecare.org.uk

Meningitis

1) Meningitis CYMRU aims to advance the education of the public in Wales in all matters relating to meningitis and provides support to individuals and families in Wales affected by meningitis and associated diseases. www.meningitiscymru.org

2) Meningitis Trust: 24 hour, 365 day a year nurse-led helpline offering facts, information and support to people affected by meningitis and meningococcal septicaemia. Tel. 0845 120 4886. www.meningitis-trust.org.uk

Mental health/illness

1) The Schizophrenia Association of Great Britain, Bryn Hyfryd, The Crescent, Bangor, Gwynedd, LL57 2AG. Tel. 01248 354048. www.sagb.co.uk

2) Mind: Tel. 0845 766 0163. www.mind.org.uk

3) Emental mental health website with information, news and discussions relevant to schizophrenia and related psychoses, Alzheimer's disease and other dementias, depression and bipolar disorder. www.emental-health.com

4) The Mental Health Foundation undertakes ground-breaking research into mental health in UK. Latest news and events on mental health issues, as well as information on problems, treatments and strategies for living with mental distress. Tel. 0207 802 0300. www.mentalhealth.org.uk

5) Young Minds: a national charity concerned with the mental health of children and young people. Tel. 0800 018 2138. www.youngminds.org.uk

Migraine

1) Migraine Action Association gives information on aspects of migraine and other headaches and treatment currently available and support for people with migraine and their families. Tel. 01536 461333. www.migraine.org.uk

Multiple sclerosis

1) Multiple Sclerosis Society gives help, support, advice and information. Helpline. Tel. 0808 800 8000. www.mssociety.org.uk

2) Multiple Sclerosis Society South Wales region. Tel. 01443 815977

3) Multiple Sclerosis Society Wales Cymru. Tel. 01656 645999

Parkinson's disease

1) The PDS national freephone helpline is one of the main sources of information for people who have just been diagnosed

with Parkinson's disease. Registered nurses provide support, information and a listening ear. Tel. 0808 800 0303. www.parkinsons.org.uk

Phobias

1) National Phobias Society (NPS) is a registered charity for sufferers of agrophobia and for those affected by anxiety disorder. Run by sufferers and ex-sufferers. Tel. 0870 7700 456. www.md.org.uk

2) No Panic aims to aid the relief and rehabilitation of those people suffering from panic attacks, phobias, obsessive compulsive disorders and other related anxiety disorders, including tranquilliser withdrawal, and provides support. Tel. 0808 808 0545. www.nopanic.org.uk.

Skin diseases

1) The National Eczema Society, Unit 26, Imex Business Centre, Balme Road, Cleckheaton, BD19 4EZ, provides support and information, including fact sheets and videos, to help improve the quality of life for people with eczema and their carers. Represents the needs of the people with eczema and their carers and raises funds for research to identify causes and potential cures. Tel. 0870 241 3604, Fax 01274 871 574. email helpline@eczema.org www.eczema.org

Smoking

1) NHS Smoking helpline offers practical, helpful and friendly advice to individuals wanting to give up smoking, as well as details of local stop-smoking services. Health professionals can order literature from helpline. Tel. 0800 169 0169. www.givingupsmoking.co.uk

Spastic (cerebral palsy)

1) Scope helpline for people with cerebral palsy: Tel. 0808 800 3333. www.scope.org.uk

Stroke

1) Different Strokes provides young stroke survivors with access to exercise facilities, practical information packs, counselling services, benefits rights, information on education and special training and work opportunities. Tel. 0845 130 7172. www.differentstrokes.co.uk

2) The Stroke Association provides support and a helpline for people who have had a stroke and their families and carers. Tel. 0845 303 3100. www.stroke.org.uk

Tuberculosis

1) Sclerosis Association provides support, advice on management, counselling, health needs, social services, benefits and education. Tel. 01527 871898. www.tuberus-sclerosis.org.uk